Breaking the Code

Jerome D. Lebo

SRA McGraw-Hill

Columbus, Ohio

A Division of The McGraw·Hill Companies

www.sra4kids.com

SRA/McGraw-Hill

A Division of The **McGraw·Hill** *Companies*

Copyright © 1999 by SRA/McGraw-Hill.

Send all inquiries to:
SRA/McGraw-Hill
8787 Orion Place
Columbus, Ohio 43204-4027

Printed in the United States of America.

ISBN 0-02-831132-9

10 11 12 13 14 15 DBH 07 06 05 04 03 02

Sounds and Their Spellings

Lesson	Vowel Sounds		Consonant Sounds		Page
4	a i		m t n r p		1
5	e o u				6
6	ē	(ē) (ee) (ea)	s h w	(w_)	9
7			f th l d r z	(f) (ph) (th) (th) (r) (wr_) (z) (_s)	12
8	ī	(ī) (i_e) (_igh) (_ȳ)	n	(n) (kn_)	17
9			v sh		22
10	ā	(ā) (a_e) (ai_) (_ay)	b		27

Stories

a	a	j	j	s	s	A	A	J	J	S	S
b	b	k	k	t	t	B	B	K	K	T	T
c	c	l	l	u	u	C	C	L	L	U	U
d	d	m	m	v	v	D	D	M	M	V	V
e	e	n	n	w	w	E	E	N	N	W	W
f	f	o	o	x	x	F	F	O	O	X	X
g	g	p	p	y	y	G	G	P	P	Y	Y
h	h	q	q	z	z	H	H	Q	Q	Z	Z
i	i	r	r			I	I	R	R		

NOTE: The first three lessons of this Program are preliminary and do not involve the use of the Workbook.

Consonant Sound **m**   (Monkey)

_____   as in ***monkey***

Consonant Sound **t**   (Timer)

_____   as in ***timer***

1

Consonant Sound n   *(Nose)*

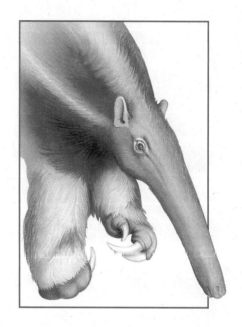

_____   as in ***nose***

Consonant Sound r   *(Robot)*

_____   as in ***robot***

Consonant Sound **p**   *(Popcorn)*

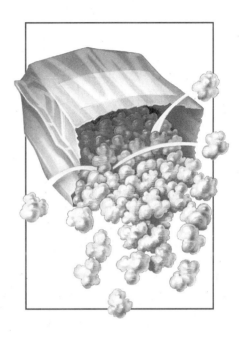

_____   as in ***popcorn***

Vowel Sound **a_**   *(Lamb)*

This sound is often called "short ***a***." It can also be written with a mark: ***ă***.

_____   as in ***lamb***

3

Vowel Sound i_ *(Pig)*

This sound is often called "short *i*." It can also be written with a mark: ĭ.

_____   as in **pig**

m m   p p

m m   p p

t t   a a

t t   a a

n n   i i

n n   i i

r r   r r

When you have finished tracing and writing the new spellings, cover what you have done. Then try to write them on the extra lines without looking at the Sound Spelling Cards or the sounds pages.

Vowel Sound e_ *(Hen)*

This sound is often called "short **e**." It can also be written with a mark: ĕ.

_____ as in **hen**

Vowel Sound o_ *(Fox)*

This sound is often called "short **o**." It can also be written with a mark: ŏ.

_____ as in **fox**

Vowel Sound u_ *(Tugboat)*

This sound is often called "short *u*." It can also be written with a mark: *ŭ*.

_____ as in *tugboat*

e____ e____

e____ e____

o____ o____

o____ o____

u____ u____

u____ u____

When you have finished tracing and writing the new spellings, cover what you have done. Then try to write them on the extra lines without looking at the Sound Spelling Cards or the sounds pages.

8

Consonant Sound **s** *(Sausages)*

_____ as in *sausages*

Consonant Sound **h_** *(Hound)*

_____ as in *hound*

Consonant Sound w_ *(Washer)*

_____ as in ***washer***

Vowel Sound ē *(Long e)*

This sound is called "long *e*." That is also the name of the card. Here are four ways to spell it. Your teacher will help you name the spellings.

_____ as in ***me***

_____ as in ***see***

_____ as in ***eat***

s   s   ē   ē

ᴧ   ᴧ   ē   ē

h_   h_   ee   ee

h_   h_   ee   ee

w_   w_   ea   ea

w_   w_   ea   ea

When you have finished tracing and writing the new spellings, cover what you have done. Then try to write them on the extra lines without looking at the Sound Spelling Cards or the sounds pages.

Consonant Sound f *(Fan)*

In some words this sound is spelled **ph**.

_____ as in *fan*

_____ as in *phone*

Consonant Sounds th and <u>th</u> *(Thing)*

The spelling **th** sometimes stands for a voiceless sound, as in **thing**, and sometimes for a voiced sound, as in **<u>th</u>ese**. In reading a word without markings, try to sound the spelling both ways.

_____ as in **thing**

_____ as in **<u>th</u>ese**

Consonant Sound l *(Lion)*

_____   as in ***lion***

Consonant Sound d *(Dinosaur)*

_____   as in ***dinosaur***

Consonant Sound r   *(Robot)*

At the beginning of some words or syllables, this sound is spelled **wr_**.

_____   as in ***robot***

_____   as in ***wreath***

Consonant Sound z   *(Zipper)*

Sometimes the letter **s** has this sound. Watch for the voice bar underneath it.

_____   as in ***zipper***

_____   as in ***weed**s**

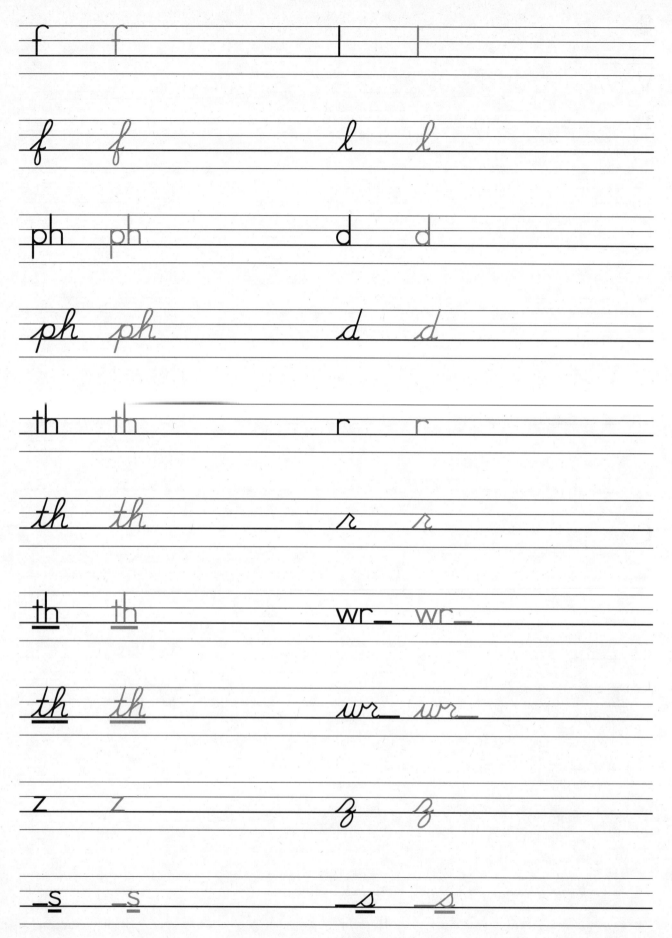

Vowel Sound ī (Long i)

This sound is often called "long *i*." It has four spellings.

_____ as in *I*

_____ as in *tide*

_____ as in *light*

_____ as in *my*

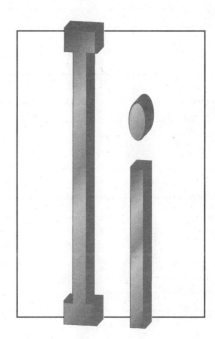

Consonant Sound n (Nose)

At the beginning of **some** words and syllables, this sound is spelled **kn_**.

_____ as in *nose*

_____ as in *knee*

ī ī   -ȳ -ȳ

ī ī   -ȳ -ȳ

i_e i_e   n n

i_e i_e   n n

_igh _igh   kn_ kn_

_igh _igh   kn_ kn_

When you have finished tracing and writing the new spellings, cover what you have done. Then try to write them on the extra lines without looking at the Sound Spelling Cards or the sounds page.

Reading Words

Your teacher will tell you how to work with the words on this page.

Level 1

1. wire	line	pine	mine	
2. wife	wi<u>s</u>e	wide	wild	
3. mile	tile	rile	pile	
4. sight	might	mild	map	
5. sire	sigh	size	sit	
6. sat	sight	sad		
7. sine	right	wrist		
8. ri<u>s</u>e	right	ride		
9. nee_	nea_	nea_	knee	
10. need	neat	near	kneel	
11. mist	twist	list	must	trust
12. fine	fight	fire	file	
13. fly	flie<u>s</u>	fry	frie<u>s</u>	

Level 2

14. thu<u>d</u>	**18.** smear	
15. drie<u>s</u>	**19.** sped	
16. trie<u>s</u>	**20.** steer	
17. fried	**21.** slide<u>s</u>	

22. strife	**27.** stride<u>s</u>
23. sphere	**28.** sneer
24. healed	**29.** reef
25. feared	**30.** retreat (re·<u>treat</u>′)
26. spleen	**31.** lease

Sentences

Level 1

1. I cut my knee last night.

2. I'll ride ten miles at night.

3. He'll hear me sneeze.

4. He lit a tiny fire.

5. That seal isn't wild.

6. The tired deer swam the stream.

Levels 2 & 3

7. He smears the mud on the tiles.

8. The tired knight fell in defeat.

9. We'll steer near the right side of the street.

1

2

3

4

5

6

7

8

9

10

11

12

13

Consonant Sound **v** *(Vacuum Cleaner)*

_____ as in *vacuum*

Consonant Sound **sh** *(Shell)*

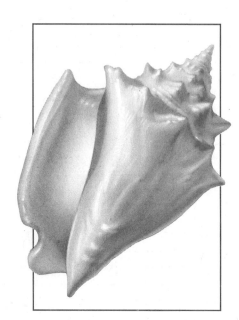

_____ as in *shell*

v   v

_N_   _N_

sh   sh

_sh_   _sh_

When you have finished tracing and writing the new spellings, cover what you have done. Then try to write them on the extra lines without looking at the Sound Spelling Cards or the sounds page.

23

Reading Words

Say the sound of *ee, igh, ea*. Watch for these spellings as you read the words below. Look for words like *nine*, too. The *e* is silent, but it signals the main vowel to say its name.

Level 1

1. she'll   she's   sheets   streets

2. eel   veal   reveal (re·veal')

3. shin   shun

4. nine   night

5. five   hive   I've

6. Eve   leave   we've   we'll   we're

7. fine   line   dine   wine

8. wife   wives   life   lives

9. leaf   leaves   fear   fears

Level 2

10. Nile

11. weave

12. shy

13. hives

14. drives

15. desire (de·sire')

16. trees

17. mean

24

18. shear<u>s</u>

19. vile

20. sheer

21. sleeve

22. reared

23. sheen

24. finite (<u>fi</u>′·nite)

25. sheaf

26. ream

27. steep

Sentences

Level 1

1. We've seen the sea in films.

2. She'll shine the light on the trees.

3. We'll need nine seeds for each pot.

4. He'll find a line and fish upstream.

5. The firelight shines on the glass.

6. We'll give Neal the flashlight.

Levels 2 & 3

7. He'll drive near the Nile.

8. The deer seems timid.

9. She'll stop at the levee.

1

2

3

4

5

6

7

8

9

10

11

12

13

Vowel Sound ā (Long a)

This sound is often called "long *a*." It has four spellings.

_____ as in **able**

_____ as in **ate**

_____ as in **aid**

_____ as in **may**

Consonant Sound b (Basketball)

_____ as in **basketball**

ā   ā   _ay _ay

ā   ā   _ay _ay

a_e a_e   b   b

a_e a_e   b   b

ai_ ai_   ai_ ai_

When you have finished tracing and writing the new spellings, cover what you have done. Then try to write them on the extra lines without looking at the Sound Spelling Cards or the sounds pages.

The One-Dot Vowel Sound: ȧ ė ȯ

If there is a vowel in the word list to which a dot has been added, pronounce that vowel by saying **uh**,

mȯther   *ȧway*

Sometimes a dot has been added to a two-letter spelling like **eȯ**:

dungeȯn

In such a spelling, pronounce only the letter that is marked with the dot.

Reading Words

Level 1

1. sa_e   saint   sale   sane

2. save   sail   bait   bale

3. alive (ȧ•<u>live</u>′)   away (ȧ•<u>way</u>′)

4. able (<u>ā</u>′ ble)   table (<u>ta</u>′ ble)

5. waded (<u>wad</u>′ ėd)   waited (<u>wait</u>′ ėd)

6. frighten (<u>fright</u>′ ėn)   frightened (<u>fright</u>′ ėned)

7. weasel (<u>wea</u>′ sėl)   seaweed (<u>sea</u>′ weed)

8. behind (bė•<u>hīnd</u>′)   beside (bė•<u>side</u>′)

9. shale

10. knife

11. tighten (<u>tight</u>′ ėn)

12. behave (bė·<u>have</u>′)

13. base ten

14. fable (f<u>ā</u>′ ble)

15. Bible (B<u>ī</u>′ ble)

16. rifle (r<u>ī</u>′ fle)

Can you find three words that start with the prefix **be-**?

Can you find two that start with a prefix that has only one letter and says **uh**?

Can you find three words that end with the suffix **-ed**?

Can you find two that end with the suffix **-en**?

Which ones begin with the prefix **re-**?

Which ones end with the suffix **-ed**?

Which ones end with the suffix **-ness**?

Which ones end with the suffix **-ful**?

Write the prefixes and suffixes in the blanks.

Level 3

	Prefixes	Suffixes
17. resealed (rē·<u>sealed</u>′)	_____	_____
18. retrained (rē·<u>trained</u>′)	_____	_____
19. remained (rē·<u>mained</u>′)	_____	_____
20. daylight (<u>day</u>′ light)	_____	_____
21. firelight (<u>fire</u>′ light)	_____	_____

30

	Prefixes	**Suffixes**
22. faintness (<u>faint</u>′ nėss)	_____	_____
23. inhale (in·<u>hale</u>′)	_____	_____
24. shameful (<u>shame</u>′ ful)	_____	_____
25. timetable (time·<u>tā</u>′ ble)	_____	_____
26. wasteful (<u>wāste</u>′ ful)	_____	_____

Sentences

Level 1

1. We waded in the sea.

2. The flames flared high.

3. We braved the freeway traffic.

4. He hid beneath the table.

5. She set a tight timetable.

6. The screams frightened him away.

Levels 2 & 3

7. They debated the entire night.

8. The fable seemed real, but dated.

9. He laid the rifle near the fire and retreated.

1

2

3

4

5

6

7

8

9

10

11

12

13

Vowel Sound ō   *(Long o)*

This sound is often called "long *o*." It has four spellings.

_____	as in **go**
_____	as in **rode**
_____	as in **oats**
_____	as in **low**

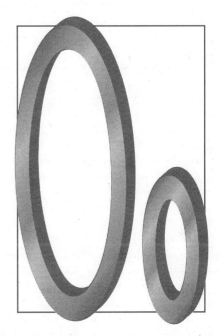

Consonant Sound g   *(Gopher)*

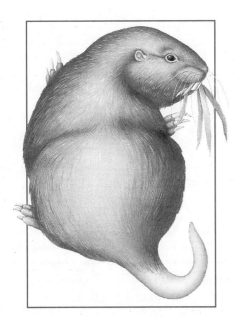

_____   as in **gopher**

ō   ō   _ōw   _ōw

ō   ō   _ōur   _ōur

o_e   o_e   g   g

o_e   o_e   g   g

oa_   oa_   oa_   oa_

When you have finished tracing and writing the new spellings, cover what you have done. Then try to write them on the extra lines without looking at the Sound Spelling Cards or the sounds page.

Reading Words

Say the sounds of   **oa_**   **_ōw**   **ai_**   **_ay**   **ea**   **ee**
Watch for these spellings as you read the words below.

Level 1

1. lone	float	bōw		
2. bone	boat	bowl		
3. roam	rove	roar		
4. road	ro<u>s</u>e	roast		
5. go	no	so		or
nor	for			
6. hole	home	hose		
7. gift	graft	Gai_		gruff
8. gave	gate	Gail		game
9. grōw	slōw	flōw		blōw
10. stay	strip	street		stripe
11. eagle (<u>ea</u>′ gle)		beagle (<u>bea</u>′ gle)		

35

12. alone (á·<u>lone</u>′)   **16.** mode

13. ago (á·<u>go</u>′)   **17.** legal (<u>lē</u>′ gál)

14. below (bė·<u>lōw</u>′)   **18.** diode (<u>di</u>′ ode)

15. besides (bė·<u>sides</u>′)   **19.** organ (<u>or</u>′ gán)

Now circle two words that begin with the prefix *a-*.

Now circle two words that begin with the prefix *be-*.

Level 3

20. needle (<u>nee</u>′ dle)   **25.** tyrant (<u>tȳ</u>′ ránt)

21. title (<u>ti</u>′ tle)   **26.** absorb (ab·<u>sorb</u>′)

22. total (<u>tō</u>′ tál)   **27.** denominator (dė·<u>nom</u>′ in·ā·tor)

23. biome (<u>bi</u>′ ome)   **28.** devoted (dė·<u>vōt</u>′ ėd)

24. shoveled (<u>shȯv</u>′ ėled)   **29.** rotated (<u>rō</u>′ tāt·ėd)

Now circle three words that end with the suffix *-ed.*

Sentences

1. That wind erodes the sand day by day.

2. His laptop is in sleep mode.

3. She gave me those roses.

4. We gave the beagle a bone.

5. The goat strayed near the street.

6. We'll wait beside the gate.

Levels 2 & 3

7. Freon erodes the ozone supply.

8. Spores can be grown in the lab.

9. The teacher rotated the globe.

1

2

3   4

5   6

7   8

9   10

11

12

13

Consonant Sound y_ *(Yak)*

When **y** begins a word or a syllable, it is a consonant.

_____   as in **yak**

Vowel Sound ū *(Long u)*

This sound is often called "long **u**." It has three spellings.

_____   as in **unite**

_____   as in **mule**

_____   as in **few**

y_ y_   u_e u_e

y_ y_   u_e u_e

ū ū   _ew _ew

ū ū   _ew _ew

When you have finished tracing and writing the new spellings, cover what you have done. Then try to write them on the extra lines without looking at the Sound Spelling Cards or the sounds page.

Vowel Sound o͞o   *(Goo)*

This sound is almost like "long *u*." If an unfamiliar word is spelled with *u_e* or *_ew*, try the sound o͞o first. Then try the sound *ū*.

_____ as in *goo*

_____ as in ***Ruth***

_____ as in ***rule***

_____ as in ***grew***

Review of Sounds

Say these sounds:

1. ē   ph   ā   z   igh   (Name each spelling.)

2. w_   ee   d   i_e   a_e   (Name each card.)

3. ė   _ȳ   kn_   h_   à   (Name each spelling.)

Now build a word around each spelling.

_ew   u_e

Can you say all the sounds on the page without a mistake?

ōō   ōō   _ew   _ew

ōō   ōō   _ew   _ew

ṳ̄   ṳ̄   u_e   u_e

ṳ̄̄   ṳ̄̄   u_e   u_e

When you have finished tracing and writing the new spellings, cover what you have done. Then try to write them on the extra lines without looking at the Sound Spelling Cards or the sounds page.

Reading Words

Level 1

Circle five words in which _*ew* says $\bar{oo}$.
Circle two in which it says $\bar{u}$.

1. yes   yet   yodel   yap

2. Ruth   rule   rude

3. loose   goose   tooth   room

4. food   fool   soon   moon

5. use   few   fuse   mew

6. grew   threw   drew   dew

7. blew   blue   glue   true   due

8. hoe   toe   doe

Level 2

9. thrive

10. monsoon (mon·soon′)

11. roommate (room′ mate)

12. human (hu′ man)

13. bugle (bu′ gle)

14. noodle (noo′ dle)

15. pupil (pu′ pil)

16. pupa (pu′ pa)

43

	Prefixes	**Suffixes**
17. fearful (fear' ful)	_____	_____
18. terrorism (terr' or·ism)	_____	_____
19. safest (saf' ėst)	_____	_____
20. refuse (rė·fuse')	_____	_____
21. define (dė·fine')	_____	_____
22. delay (dė·lay')	_____	_____
23. tasteful (taste' ful)	_____	_____
24. grateful (grate' ful)	_____	_____
25. brightest (bright' ėst)	_____	_____
26. delegates (del' ĕ·gates)	_____	_____

Now circle prefixes *re-* and *de-*.

Now circle suffixes *-ful* and *-est*.

Sentences

Level 1

1. The fuse seemed loose.

2. I'll see you soon.

3. Our bus needed fuel.

4. The old goose ate the food.

5. We'll meet near the zoo tonight.

6. We need a tube of glue.

Levels 2 & 3

7. The goose is a migratory animal.

8. The 747 gained altitude rapidly.

9. Let's fly to New Zealand.

1

2

3

4

5

6

7

8

9

10

11

12

13

Unaccented _y and _ï_ *(Long e)*

When *y* is at the end of a word like **baby**, it says ē. The plural **babies** has the same sound, but the *y* has changed to *i*.

ē

ee

ea

_____ as in **baby**

_____ as in **babies**

Three sounds of y

y_ Beginning **y** says y_, as in **yo-yo**.

ī Final **y** says ī if it is the only vowel in the word, as in **fly**.

ē Final **y** says ē very softly in words like **baby**.

Spelling Rule

Final **y** changes to *i* when we add suffixes like **-es**, **-ed**, **-er**, **-est**.

Signals e, i, and y   *(Signals)*

The letters *y* and *i* can tell the main vowel to say its name, just as *e* does. But if the main vowel is too far away, it doesn't obey, like the *a* in **happen, tapping,** or **happy.**

The vowel in an unaccented syllable usually doesn't obey either, like the *i* in **engine.**

Signals

_____   as in *safest*

_____   as in *waving*

_____   as in *baby*

Review of Sounds

Say these sounds:

1. ī   f   ea   t   ȯ
    (Name each spelling.)

2. ai_   s   _y   _ï_   wr_
    (Name each card.)

3. o_e   sh   _ay   oa_   ōō
    (Name each spelling.)

What are the two sounds of the letter **s**?
What are the two sounds of the spelling **th**?

ē ē   ea ea

ē ē   ea ea

ee ee   _y _y

ee ee   _y _y

_ï _ï   _ï _ï

When you have finished tracing and writing the new spellings, cover what you have done. Then try to write them on the extra lines without looking at the Sound Spelling Cards or the sounds pages.

Reading Words

1. rainy (<u>rain</u>′ y)   greedy (<u>greed</u>′ y)

2. shady (<u>shad</u>′ y)   shiny (<u>shin</u>′ y)

3. easy (<u>eas</u>′ y)   easiest (<u>eas</u>′ ï·ėst)

4. lady (<u>la</u>′ dy)   ladies (<u>la</u>′ dïe<u>s</u>)

5. duty (<u>du</u>′ ty)   duties (<u>du</u>′ tïe<u>s</u>)

6. safely (<u>safe</u>′ ly)   gravity (<u>grăv</u>′ ĭ·ty)

7. navy (<u>na</u>′ vy)   navies (<u>na</u>′ vïe<u>s</u>)

Draw an arrow whenever a signal makes the main vowel say its name:

shady   *safely*   *navies*

Watch for suffixes like **-y, -ly, -est, -es**. How many root words can you find?

---

8. theory (<u>theo</u>′ ry)   12. idle (<u>ī</u>′ dle)

9. holiest (<u>ho</u>′ lï·ėst)   13. idly (<u>ī</u>′ dly)

10. immunity (im·<u>mu</u>′ nĭ·ty)   14. able (<u>ā</u>′ ble)

11. polygon (<u>pol</u>′ y·gon)   15. ably (<u>ā</u>′ bly)

	Root Word	Suffix
16. botany (bŏ′ tan·y)	_____	_____
17. wisely (wise′ ly)	_____	_____
18. density (den′ sĭ·ty)	_____	_____
19. monopoly (mo·nop′ o·ly)	_____	_____
20. treaty (treat′ y)	_____	_____
21. shiniest (shin′ ĭ·ėst)	_____	_____
22. grimy (grim′ y)	_____	_____
23. grimiest (grim′ ĭ·ėst)	_____	_____

Sentences

Level 1

1. He is usually on duty here.

2. The rain made the road shiny.

3. The treaty was signed illegally.

4. He knows the truth.

Levels 2 & 3

5. She had developed immunity to the disease.

6. Zoology is the study of animal life.

7. Botany is the study of plant life.

1

2

3   4

5   6

7   8

9   10

11

12

13

Vowel Sound er   *(Robot)*

The spellings *er, ir,* and *ur* all have the same sound. Say them with your mouth in the same position as for the consonant sound *r,* but say them louder.

r   wr___

_____ as in **Bert**

_____ as in **dirt**

_____ as in **hurt**

Complete these words by inserting a spelling from those above:

_____en   (a bird)

_____ut   (a groove in the road)

cl_____k   (a kind of worker)

h_____dle   (something to get over)

_____n   (a container)

b_____th   (arrival of a new life)

r   r   ur   ur

er   er   wr_   wr_

ir   ir   ir   ir

When you have finished tracing and writing the new spellings, cover what you have done. Then try to write them on the extra lines without looking at the Sound Spelling Cards or the sounds page.

Reading Words

1. bird   tern   burst

2. hurt   herd   shirt   hurry (hur´ ry)

3. fir   fur   first   urn

4. lower (low´ er)   faster (fast´ er)   higher (high´ er)

5. fly   flier (fli´ er)   fertile (fer´ tile)

6. dry   drier (dri´ er)   shy   sir

7. lazy (la´ zy)   pretend (pre·tend´)   lazier (la´ zï·er)

8. sleepy (sleep´ y)   perfect (per´ fect)   sleepier (sleep´ ï·er)

> In words like *fly,* final *y* says *i.* Can the *i* sound be heard in *flier,* too?
>
> In words like *lazy,* final *y* says *e* softly. Can this *e* sound be heard in *lazier,* too?

Prefixes: *pre-*   *re-*   *de-*
Suffixes: *-ed*   *-y*   *-er*   *-s*   *-ant*   *-est*   *-ly*

Level 2

		Prefixes:	Suffixes:
9.	spared	_____	_____
10.	stirred	_____	_____
11.	poverty (pov′ er·ty)	_____	_____
12.	thirsty (thirst′ y)	_____	_____
13.	artery (ar′ ter·y)	_____	_____
14.	return (rė·turn′)	_____	_____
15.	diversity (div·er′ sĭ·ty)	_____	_____
16.	vertebra (ver′ tē·brȧ)	_____	_____

Level 3

		Prefixes:	Suffixes:
17.	millimeter (mil′ li·me·ter)	_____	_____
18.	invertebrate (in·ver′ tė·brate)	_____	_____
19.	thermometer (ther·mŏ′ me·ter)	_____	_____
20.	thirstiest (thirst′ ï·ėst)	_____	_____
21.	dirtiest (dirt′ ï·ėst)	_____	_____
22.	prevailed (prė·vailed′)	_____	_____
23.	repairs (rė·pairs′)	_____	_____
24.	sprightly (spright′ ly)	_____	_____
25.	deserted (dė·sert′ ėd)	_____	_____

Sentences

1. Don't desert us until after dessert.

2. The properties of matter are well-known.

3. What part of a meter is one millimeter?

4. An herbivore eats only plant matter.

5. Get underneath the overpass!

Levels 2 & 3

6. She decided to terminate her investments.

7. I interpret interest in this matter as self-serving.

Proverbs

1. If it's not broken, don't fix it.

2. When in doubt, tell the truth.

3. Always do right. This will gratify some people and astonish the rest.

1

2

3

4

5

6

7

8

9

10

11

12

13

Vowel Sound i_ (Pig)

This sound is often called "short *i*." It can also be written with a mark: *ĭ*. Watch for this mark. It tells you that the *i* is disobeying a signal.

_____ as in *is*

i   i

i   *i*

When you have finished tracing and writing the new spelling, turn the page. Then try to write it on the extra lines without looking at the Sound Spelling Cards or the sounds page.

Reading Words

Level 1

1. miss	didn't	wind	dip
2. with	will	wish	wit
3. hit	mist	hi<u>s</u>	list

infer (in·<u>fer</u>′)   imply (im·<u>ply</u>′)

4. stiff	still	sniff

differ (<u>dif</u>′ fer)   mint

5. pale	pail	paid	paint
6. till	tile	fill	file

7. spider (<u>spi</u>′ der)   additive (<u>ad</u>′ dĭ·tĭve)

speediest (<u>speed</u>′ ï·ĕst)

Level 2

8. volume (<u>vol</u>′ ume)   **12.** deposit (de·<u>pos</u>′ it)

9. asleep (à·<u>sleep</u>′)   **13.** wisdom (<u>wis</u>′ dom)

10. British (<u>Brĭt</u>′ ish)   **14.** observe (ob·<u>serve</u>′)

11. Merlin (<u>Mer</u>′ lin)   **15.** Brazil (Brà·<u>zil</u>′)

Watch for the new sound, marked with a curve: ĭ. Sometimes it disobeys the signals.

16. Italy (<u>It</u>′ a̍·ly)

17. invaders (in·<u>vad</u>′ er<u>s</u>)

18. astronomer (a̍·<u>stron</u>′ o·mer)

19. sizzle (<u>siz</u>′ zle)

20. atmosphere (<u>at</u>′ mo·sphere)

21. prison (<u>pris</u>′ on)

22. miserable (<u>mĭs</u>′ er·a̍·ble)

23. hibernate (<u>hi</u>′ ber·nate)

24. lateral (<u>lat</u>′ er·a̍l)

25. university (ū·ni·<u>ver</u>′ si·ty)

Proverbs

1. Live and learn.

2. Time is money.

3. Rome wasn't built in a day.

There are no more sentences from here on.
You will be reading stories instead.

Merlin

There once lived a wizard named Merlin. Merlin had great powers of magic. He was also very wise. When King Pendragon was looking for his long lost son, Merlin made up a test to find him. He put a sword in stone and cast a spell so that only the prince could pull it out. Many men tried to take the sword from the stone, but none could. King Pendragon waited and wished his son would come. Then a young boy named Arthur came to town. When he took the sword, the others thought it was a trick. Merlin knew Arthur was the real prince. He also knew that Arthur would be a great king.

Words to Watch

magic   thought

sword   powers

trick   Pendragon

1. The selection gives two characteristics of Merlin. What are they?

2. How did Merlin get the sword to stay in the stone?

3. How is the test in this story different from the ones you take in school?

4. Did the sword have a name? If the selection doesn't say, how could you find out?

_____
_____
_____

_____
_____

_____
_____
_____

_____
_____
_____

_____
_____
_____

Dictation

1

2

3　　　　　　　　　　　　　4

5　　　　　　　　　　　　　6

7　　　　　　　　　　　　　8

9　　　　　　　　　　　　　10

11

12

13

65

Consonant Sound k   *(Camera)*

The spelling **_ck** is used only after "short" vowels *a_, e_, i_, o_, u_*.

_____   as in **kite**

_____   as in **coat**

_____   as in **sick**

Consonant Sound _ng   *(Gong)*

This sound is heard in words like **think**, **sank**, **tongs**, and **rung**.

_____   as in **gong**

66

k   k   _ck   _ck

_k _k   _ck _ck

c   c   _ng   _ng

_c _c   _ng _ng

When you have finished tracing and writing the new spellings, cover what you have done. Then try to write them on the extra lines without looking at the Sound Spelling Cards or the sounds page.

Reading Words

1. kick   pick   stick   trick

2. sing   bring   thing   string

     king

3. sink   think   drink   kink

4. oak   stroke   stroking (<u>strok</u>′ ing)

     coastline (<u>coast</u>′ line)

5. sitting (<u>sit</u>′ ting)   stirring (<u>stir</u>′ ring)

     silly (<u>sil</u>′ ly)   faking (<u>fak</u>′ ing)

6. shining (<u>shin</u>′ ing)   hitting (<u>hit</u>′ ting)

7. case   came   became (bė•<u>came</u>′)   stock

Draw arrows to show the action of the signals *e, i,* and *y*:

       case   *stroking*   *lazy*

Does the *y* in **silly** make the main vowel say its name? No, because it is too far away to act.

Why do we double the *t* in **sit** before adding *-ing*?

       silly   *sitting*

---

8. missed

9. magnet (mag′ net)

10. current (cur′ rent)

11. middle (mid′ dle)

12. fungus (fun′ gus)

13. electron (e·lec′ tron)

14. trickle (trick′ le)

15. concave (con′ cave)

Level 3

Root Words

16. composer (com·pos′ er) _____

17. cartographer (car·tog′ raph·er) _____

18. flickering (flick′ er·ing) _____

19. kinetic (kin·et′ ic) _____

20. inorganic (in·or·gan′ ic) _____

21. glucose (glu′ cose) _____

22. continuous (con·tin′ ū·ous) _____

23. accompany (ac·com′ pa·ny) _____

24. container (con·tain′ er) _____

25. osmosis (os·mo′ sis) _____

Now write the root words.

Proverbs

1. Haste makes waste.

2. Easy come, easy go.

3. Don't cry over spilled milk.

Mount Kilauea

Mount Kilauea is a volcano. Near its peak is a crater almost two miles wide. Bright red lava flows out of the crater and trickles out of smaller holes in the sides of the volcano. It forms rivers that flow to the Pacific Ocean, killing all in its path.

Facts about Kilauea:

In 1950, Kilauea spit out lava that could pave an 8-lane highway two times around Earth.

In 1959, Kilauea shot lava 2000 feet high. That's more than 1½ times taller than the Empire State Building.

In 1985, a man was standing on a crust of lava when it cracked and he fell in. He was badly burned but he lived. His clothing kept him alive until a man with him pulled him to safety.

Words to Watch

forms	Mount Kilauea	crater
killing	facts	crust
cracked	around	Pacific Ocean

Comprehension

1. Where is the crater?

2. What is another way of saying "two miles wide"?

3. Read about what Kilauea did in 1950. What mathematical facts would you have to have to calculate how much lava was spit out?

4. How tall is the Empire State Building? Could you find out from this article? How could you find out in another way?

Dictation

1

2

3   4

5   6

7   8

9   10

11

12

13

Vowel Sound a_   *(Lamb)*

This sound is often called "short *a*." It can also be written with a mark: ă

_____   as in ***lamb***

Consonant Sound s spelled c   *(Sausages)*

The letter *c* says *s* when there is a signal after it.

_____ as in ***face***

_____ as in ***icing***

_____ as in ***lacy***

a_ a_   ci ci

a_ a_   ci ci

ce ce   cy cy

ce ce   cy cy

When you have finished tracing and writing the new spellings, cover what you have done. Then try to write them on the extra lines without looking at the Sound Spelling Cards or the sounds page.

Reading Words

1. bad   sag   bank   bat

2. flat   flap   flapped   slapped

3. race   face   place   space

4. ice   mice   nice   twice

5. can   can't   candle (<u>can</u>′ dle)

6. icy (ī′ cy)   city (cĭ′ ty)   icing (<u>ic</u>′ ing)   species (<u>spe</u>′ cïe<u>s</u>)

7. fancy (<u>fan</u>′ cy)   cancer (<u>can</u>′ cer)   dancing (<u>danc</u>′ ing)   scent

---

Remember that a signal *e*, *i*, or *y* can make *c* say *s*:

prancing   ***Nancy***

Sometimes a signal acts in two ways at the same time:

face   ***icing***

What words in the list have a signal that acts in two ways?

---

8. circle (<u>cir</u>′ cle)

9. conical (<u>con</u>′ ĭ·cal)

10. complain (cȯm·<u>plain</u>′)

11. census (<u>cen</u>′ sus)

12. practice (<u>prac</u>′ tĭce)

13. craftsmen (<u>crafts</u>′ mėn)

14. cubic (<u>cu</u>′ bic)

15. mercy (<u>mer</u>′ cy)

Now circle three words in which *c* says *s*.

75

16. acute triangle (à·cute' tri' an·gle)

17. Africa (Af' ri·cà)

18. Atlantic (At·lan' tic)

19. canopy (can' ò·py)

20. precipice (prec' ĭ·pĭce)

21. magnificent (mag·nĭf' i·cent)

22. concentric (con·cen' tric)

23. epidermis (ep·ĭ·der' mis)

24. Sicily (Sĭc' i·ly)

25. cell membrane (cell mem' brane)

Now circle three more words in which **c** says **s**.

Proverbs

1. Seeing is believing.

2. Time waits for no man.

3. Don't bite the hand that feeds you.

Winter Fun

For some people, winter is a time to stay inside and drink hot chocolate. Others like to spend winter outdoors. Either way, it can be a great season for having fun.

At the mall, there is an ice skating rink. It has a lot of space to skate and to practice spinning in circles. There's even room for fancy leaps.

There are lots of other things to do in winter. Some people play ice hockey. Others like to sled or ski. Still others go ice fishing. They cut a hole in the ice and drop their line.

Even if you're one of those people who likes to stay indoors, you can still have fun in winter. Sit by a fire and look at the pretty snow outside.

Words to Watch

people

chocolate

indoors

1. What types of things can people do outside in the winter?

2. What can people do inside in the winter?

3. How are winter activities different from summer activities?

1

2

3

4

5

6

7

8

9

10

11

12

13

Consonant Sound j_ *(Jump)*

The letter **g** often says **j_** when there is a signal after it. The spelling **-dge** is used only after "short" vowels **a_, e_, i_, o_, u_**.

_____ as in *jump*

_____ as in *age*

_____ as in *giant*

_____ as in *gym*

_____ as in *bridge*

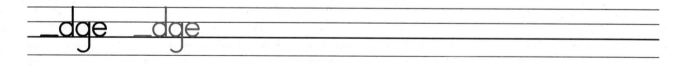

j   j

j   *j*

_dge   _dge

_dge   *_dge*

ġy   ġy

ġy   ġy

ġe   ġe

ġe   ġe

ġï   ġï

ġï   ġï

When you have finished tracing and writing the new spellings, cover what you have done. Then try to write them on the extra lines without looking at the Sound Spelling Cards or the sounds page.

Reading Words

1. joke   Janice (Jan′ ĭce)   justice (jus′ tĭce)

2. last   land   lap

3. sat   sank   sack

4. energy (en′ er·ġy)   engine (en′ ġĭne)   huge

5. jab   jute   jury (jur′ y)

6. sting   stingy (stin′ ġy)

7. package (pack′ aġe)   giant (ġī′ ant)

Watch for the effect of the signals *e*, *i*, and *y*:

age   *ginger*   *gym*

What words in the list have a signal that acts in two ways?

---

8. rangers (rān′ ġers)   **12.** merge

9. oxygen (ox′ y·ġen)   **13.** Egypt (E′ ġўpt)

10. adjacent (ad jā cėnt)   **14.** perfect (per′ fėct)

11. princess (prin′ cėss)   **15.** indigent (in′ dĭ·ġent)

Now circle two words in which **g** obeys a signal.

16. refrigerated (re·frig′ er·a·ted)

17. adjacent (a·dja′ cent)

18. genetics (gen·et′ ics)

19. scavenger (sca′ ven·ger)

20. circumference (cir·cum′ fer·ence)

21. kangaroo (kan·ga·roo′)

22. allergy (al′ ler·gy)

23. religion (re·lig′ ion)

24. Germany (Ger′ ma·ny)

25. emergency (e·mer′ gen·cy)

Now circle three words in which **g** obeys a signal.

Proverbs

1. You can't have your cake and eat it too.

2. It's later than you think.

3. Practice makes perfect.

Jazz

During the 1920s a new kind of music took America by storm. Its strong, swinging beat made people want to get up and move. So that's what people did. Everywhere, they were listening and dancing to jazz. It was the Jazz Age.

In the late 1800s, African American musicians in the south started jazz. It was a mix of work songs, spirituals, and blues. When someone died, African American marching bands played slow songs on the way to the cemetery. On the way back, they played the same songs, but they changed the beat. They added notes and changed notes. They played faster and louder.

People liked the new sound. They crowded into places where jazz was played. Sometimes musicians would stay up all night jamming, or playing music together. People like Louis Armstrong and Duke Ellington went around the world playing jazz. Huge crowds of people heard them play. They are called giants of jazz, and their music is still played today.

Words to Watch

musicians   spirituals   Louis Armstrong   Duke Ellington

1. When did jazz begin to take shape? Where?

2. What does it mean when the story says "giants of jazz"?

3. What decade marked the "Jazz Age"?

4. How many other famous jazz artists can you name?

1

2

3   **4**

5   **6**

7   **8**

9   **10**

11

12

13

Vowel Sound o_   *(Fox)*

This sound is often called "short o." It can be written with a mark: ŏ.

_____   as in **fox**

Consonant Sounds _x and _x   *(Exit Sign)*

When the letter **x** comes after a vowel, it is sometimes whispered, as in **box**, and sometimes voiced, as in **ex̲it**.

_____ = ks   as in **box**

_____ = gz   as in **ex̲it**

87

O___ O___

O___ O___

___X ___X

___X ___X

___X ___X

___X ___X

When you have finished tracing and writing the new spellings, cover what you have done. Then try to write them on the extra lines without looking at the Sound Spelling Cards or the sounds page.

Reading Words

1. ox   socks   fox   locks

2. six   ticks   fix   picks

3. Max   backs   wax   tax

4. drop   dropped   stop   stopped

5. trot   trotted (trot′ tĕd)   trotting (trot′ ting)

6. nod   nodded (nod′ dĕd)   boxing (box′ ing)

7. song   strong   along (à·long′)

sarong (sà·rong′)

Do you see any doubled consonants: **pp**, **tt**, **dd**, **rr**, **ll**, **nn**?
Mark the vowel before the double:

     trŏtted   **dĭmmer**

---

8. toxic (tox′ ic)

9. extinct (ex·tinct′)

10. tomorrow (tò·mor′ row)

11. Holland (Hol′ lànd)

12. variety (và·rī′ è·ty)

13. life expectancy (life ex·pec′tan·cy)

14. exhibit (ex·hib′ it)

15. volume (vol′ ume)

89

16. textiles (<u>tex</u>′ tiles)

17. annex (<u>an</u>′ nex)

18. complicated (<u>com</u>′ pli·cat·ėd)

19. opportunity (op·pȯr·<u>tu</u>′ ni·ty)

20. hospital (<u>hos</u>′ pi·tȧl)

21. Acropolis (A·<u>crop</u>′ ȯ·lis)

22. commonplace (<u>com</u>′ mȯn·place)

23. profitable (<u>prŏf</u>′ it·ȧ·ble)

24. convex (<u>con</u>′ vex)

25. continent (<u>con</u>′ ti·nėnt)

Proverbs

1. A man is known by the company he keeps.

2. Silence is golden.

3. Variety is the spice of life.

Tap Dancing

Tap. Tap. Tap. Tap. Can you hear it? It's a tap dance.

Tap dancers wear shoes with metal tips on the toes and heels. They tap the tips to a beat. Maybe you've seen Savion Glover tap dance. His feet go very fast. Sometimes he dances on the edges of his shoes. He may be the best dancer in this age.

Tap dancing started in America in the 1840s. It is made up of jig dancing, clog dancing, and an African beat. Later, steps were added from other dances and from ragtime and jazz steps.

Some dancers do a kind of tap dance without the tapping sound. This dance is called the "soft shoe." Soft-shoe dancers dance on sand on the floor. The sand makes a softer sound.

Words to Watch

shoes	Savion Glover	clog dancing
floor	ragtime	jig dancing

1. What is jig dancing? Where did it come from?

2. What is clog dancing? Where did it come from?

3. Highlight the words that tell where the metal tips are placed on tap shoes.

4. Highlight the three ingredients of tap dancing.

5. Read the last sentence in the story. Cross out the period and write the word "than." Then continue writing to answer the question "Than what?"

_____

_____

_____

_____

_____

_____

_____

_____

_____

_____

_____

_____

_____

_____

_____

Dictation

1

2

3   4

5   6

7   8

9   10

11

12

13

Vowel Sound e_ *(Hen)*

This sound is often called "short **e**." It can also be written with a mark: **ĕ**. It has two spellings:

_____ as in **hen**

_____ as in **head**

Consonant Sound ch *(Chipmunk)*

The spelling **-tch** is used only after "short" vowels **a_, e_, i_, o_, u_**.

_____ as in **each**

_____ as in **pitch**

e_   e_   ch   ch

e   *e*   *ch*   *ch*

_ĕa_   _ĕa_

_ĕa_   _ĕa_

_tch   _tch

tch   *tch*

When you have finished tracing and writing the new spellings, cover what you have done. Then try to write them on the extra lines without looking at the Sound Spelling Cards or the sounds page.

Reading Words

Level 1

1. tell	test	ten
2. munch	chipmunk (<u>chip</u>′ munk)	chum
3. neck	nest	next
4. chase	kitchen (<u>kitch</u>′ ėn)	China (<u>Chi</u>′ nȧ)
5. leech	batch	switch
6. read	red	ready (<u>rĕad</u>′ y)
7. head	help	heavy (<u>hĕav</u>′ y)

Suffixes: *-ed* *-en* *-er* *-ese* *-ing* *-ive* *-ize*
       -less *-ly* *-or* *-ous* *-s* *-y*

Level 2

	Root Words	Suffixes
8. oxen (<u>ŏx</u>′ ėn)	_____	_____
9. hedges (<u>hedg</u>′ ė<u>s</u>)	_____	_____
10. percentage (per·<u>cen</u>′ tage)	_____	_____
11. cobblestones (<u>cob</u>′ ble·stone<u>s</u>)	_____	_____
12. Chinese (Chī·<u>nese</u>′)	_____	_____
13. heavenly (<u>hĕav</u>′ ėn·ly)	_____	_____
14. slingshot (<u>sling</u>′ shot)	_____	_____
15. restless (<u>rest</u>′ lėss)	_____	_____

Write the root words. Write the suffixes.

	Root Words	Suffixes
16. Scotland (<u>Scot</u>′ lånd)	_____	_____
17. computer (com·<u>pu</u>′ ter)	_____	_____
18. currency (<u>cur</u>′ ren·cy)	_____	_____
19. prosperous (<u>pros</u>′ per·ous)	_____	_____
20. impeached (im·<u>peached</u>′)	_____	_____
21. inventor (in·<u>vent</u>′ or)	_____	_____
22. terrified (<u>ter</u>′ ri·fied)	_____	_____
23. pentagon (<u>pen</u>′ tå·gon)	_____	_____
24. hexagon (<u>hex</u>′ å·gon)	_____	_____
25. apologize (å·<u>pol</u>′ o·ġize)	_____	_____

Proverbs

1. Tomorrow is another day.

2. Two heads are better than one.

3. All that glitters is not gold.

Amazing Animal Facts

Zebra stripes are like fingerprints. Each zebra has its own stripe pattern. No two zebras' stripes match.

A pelican can hold up to 25 pounds of fish in its pouch. That's about the same as its weight.

A crocodile's jaws are so strong they can catch a large animal or person and pull it under water. But a crocodile can't chew, and its jaws can be tied shut with a string.

There are about 40,000 muscles in an elephant's trunk. There are 650 muscles in your entire body.

A female chaffinch makes up to 1,300 trips to gather grass, moss, and feathers for its nest. It takes about 18 days. It takes only 11 days for her eggs to hatch.

Words to Watch

jaws	pounds	pouch	weight
feathers	large	chaffinch	pounds
	crocodile	fingerprints	

Comprehension

1. How are fingerprints like zebra stripes?

2. Highlight the sentence that contains the largest number in the story.

3. Which statements make comparisons or contrasts? What are they?

4. If a crocodile can't chew, how does it eat?

5. Why might the chaffinch be so meticulous about building its nest?

1 _____ _____ _____ _____ _____

2 _____ _____ _____ _____ _____

3 _____   4 _____

5 _____   6 _____

7 _____   8 _____

9 _____   10 _____

11 _____

12 _____

13 _____

Consonant Sound wh_ *(Whale)*

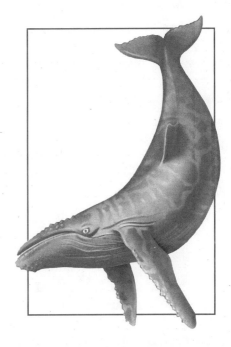

_____ as in ***whale***

Vowel Sound u_ *(Tugboat)*

This sound is often called "short *u*." It can be written with a mark: *ŭ*. If a vowel in the word list has a dot over it, try saying the sound *u_* very softly.

_____ as in ***tugboat***

_____ as in ***ȧlone***

_____ as in ***waitėd***

_____ as in ***reasȯn***

wh_   wh_   ė ė

wh_   wh_   ė ė

u_   u_   ȯ ȯ

u_   u_   ȯ ȯ

ȧ   ȧ   ȧ ȧ

When you have finished tracing and writing the new spellings, cover what you have done. Then try to write them on the extra lines without looking at the Sound Spelling Cards or the sounds page.

Review

1. What are the three sounds of the letter *y*?

2. What are the two sounds of *u_e*?

3. What letters are signals?

4. What are the three different things that signals can do?

5. What are the two sounds of *_ew*?

Reading Words

Level 1

1. while   white   when

2. stuff   stuffed   stuck

3. much   must   into

4. just   jump   judge

5. wheel   whale   mass

6. which   why   whisper (<u>whis</u>′ per)

7. even (<u>e</u>′ v<u>e</u>n)   season (<u>sea</u>′ s<u>o</u>n)

8. ecology (e·<u>col</u>′ o·gy)

9. numb

10. calcium (<u>cal</u>′ ci·um)

11. whether (<u>wheth</u>′ er)

12. succeed (suc·<u>ceed</u>′)

13. lever (<u>lĕv</u>′ er)

14. radius (<u>ra</u>′ di·us)

15. random (<u>ran</u>′ dom)

16. saliva (sȧ·<u>li</u>′ vȧ)

17. vitamin (<u>vi</u>′ tȧ·min)

18. insect (<u>in</u>′ sect)

19. cadence (ca·<u>dence</u>′)

20. metabolism (mė·<u>tab</u>′ o·lism)

21. temperature (<u>tem</u>′ per·ȧ·ture)

22. telescope (<u>tĕl</u>′ ė·scope)

23. diameter (di·<u>ă</u>′ me·ter)

24. recognized (<u>rec</u>′ ȯg·nized)

25. enthusiasm (en·<u>thū</u>′ <u>s</u>i·a<u>s</u>m)

Proverbs

1. Beggars can't be choosers.

2. Better late than never, but better never late.

3. If at first you don't succeed, try, try again.

Hula

Did you know you could tell a story without saying a word? That's what hula dancers do when they dance. Each movement of their arms, legs, and hips "says" something different. There is a reason and a meaning for every movement.

Crossing your arms in front of your chest means love. Putting your fingertips together in a roof shape in front of you means house. Waving both hands over your head says tree in the wind. When you want to tell something about the ocean, you must hold out your hands with the palms down. Then just slowly move them back and forth in front of you like waves.

What story would you tell with hula dancing?

Words to Watch

movement   house

arms   ocean

1. Describe the arm or hand positions that would indicate:
   a. house
   b. ocean
   c. love
   d. waving trees
   e. a houseboat

2. Is the hula the only storytelling dance? What others can you think of?

The Traveling Eyeball

by Patricia Grossman

Have you ever wished you had eyes in the back of your head? Most fish almost do. They have one eye on each side of their heads, one on the right and one on the left. Their eyes are about where our ears are. With their two eyes so far apart and on opposite sides of their heads, these fish can see almost everything around them. It's almost impossible for anything or anyone to sneak up on them without being seen.

Unlike most fish, people have their eyes both on one side of their heads, the front side. It's easy for someone to sneak up on us just by coming up from behind us. There is one kind of fish whose eyes, like people's eyes, are both on one side of its head. It's the halibut. But instead of both eyes being on the front side of a halibut's head, they are both on the right side. If that seems strange to you, wait. Here's something even stranger. The halibut wasn't born that way. That left eyeball *moved over the halibut's head* until it was next to the right eyeball.

When halibut eggs are laid, they look like a million soap bubbles floating on the water. Each soap bubble is one egg. A week later, each egg hatches. Now, let's follow one baby halibut through the strange changes that are soon to come.

When it is born, a halibut is very tiny. Eight halibut lined up head to tail would make a line only one inch long. Baby halibut are called *fry*. A fry has a rounded body like most fish, with one eye on the left side of its head and one eye on the right. Fry swim standing up, with their faces at the top of the water.

At the age of two weeks, a halibut's body begins its strange changes. It starts leaning over onto its left side and sinking in the water. Soon its body is no longer round but flat. It has a left side and a right side and no other sides, just like a thick piece of paper. Its right side begins to turn brown, and its left side begins to turn white. It is during this flattening and color changing that its left eye travels over its head and ends up next to its right eye.

All of these strange changes take about four months. By that time, a halibut is an inch long. It now swims on the ocean floor. Its color changes have made it harder to see. Fish and other enemies can't see it when they're above it in the water, because its brown side matches the mud. Fish and other enemies can't see it when they're below it in the water, because its white side matches the daylight coming from far above.

By now a halibut's strange changes are almost finished. From here on, all it will do is grow a lot bigger. Some halibut reach a length of fifteen feet and weigh 700 pounds! Picture the fully grown halibut swimming through the dark, silent ocean near the sea floor.

1. List all the changes that a halibut goes through as it is growing up.

2. About how long do these changes take?

3. How big can some halibut become?

Dictation

1

2

3

4

5

6

7

8

9

10

11

12

13

Consonant Sound qu_   *(Quacking)*

q
_____ = kw   as in *quacking*

Vowel Sound ow   *(Cow)*

This sound has two spellings.

_____ as in *cow*

_____ as in *out*

qu_ qu_

qu_ qu_

ow ow

ow ow

ou_ ou_

ou_ ou_

When you have finished tracing and writing the new spellings, cover what you have done. Then try to write them on the extra lines without looking at the Sound Spelling Cards or the sounds page.

Reading Words

Level 1

1. hound   house   surround (sur·<u>round</u>′)

    ground

2. crown   town   down   brown

3. grow   blow   dowel (<u>dow</u>′ el)

    bowel (<u>bow</u>′ el)

4. huge   hug   tack   take

5. quit   quick   quickly (<u>quick</u>′ ly)

6. quite   quiet (<u>quī</u>′ ėt)

7. hiding (<u>hid</u>′ ing)   hidden (<u>hid</u>′ dėn)

8. quality (qual′ i·ty)

9. quenched

10. quantum (quan′ tum)

11. thousands (thou′ sands)

12. crater (cra′ ter)

13. quaint

14. suspense (sus·pense′)

15. Quebec (Quė·bec′)

Level 3

16. Mexico (Mex′ i·co)

17. Korea (Kor·e′ à)

18. ungrateful (un·grate′ ful)

19. Jupiter (Ju′ pi·ter)

20. Japanese (Jap·à·nese′)

21. tolerance (tol′ er·ance)

22. Amsterdam (Am′ ster·dam)

23. cylinder (cy̆l′ in·der)

24. manuscript (man′ ū·script)

25. nonviolence (non·vi′ o·lence)

Proverbs

1. Half a loaf is better than no bread.

2. A friend in need is a friend indeed.

3. The more the merrier.

Earthquakes

Windows rattle. Books fall off shelves. The floor shakes. What's happening? It's an earthquake!

Earthquakes happen when rocks in the Earth's crust slide. There are about 6,000 earthquakes each year. Most of them are very small or far away from people. About 450 are so strong that you can feel them, but they don't hurt anything. About 35 create a little damage. But the rest, about 15, can create quite a bit of damage. Houses and buildings fall down. Bridges and tunnels are crunched. Gas, water, and power lines blow up, break, and fall.

Earthquakes happen very quickly. A calm, quiet day can become a shaking, quaking fright. In the United States, most earthquakes happen in California and Alaska. Builders there have learned how to make buildings safer and stronger.

Words to Watch

damage   floor   earthquake

quaking   buildings

115

1. Highlight the answer to this question: What makes an earthquake happen?

2. Highlight the words which tell where most earthquakes happen in the U.S.

3. Do we get much warning about an impending quake? Underline the sentence that tells.

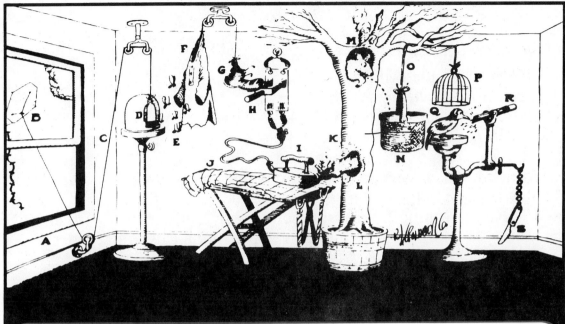

Professor Butts gets his think-tank working and evolves the simplified pencil sharpener.

Open window (**A**) and fly kite (**B**). String (**C**) lifts small door (**D**), allowing moths (**E**) to escape and eat red flannel shirt (**F**). As weight of shirt becomes less, shoe (**G**) steps on switch (**H**) which heats electric iron (**I**) and burns hole in pants (**J**).

Smoke (**K**) enters hole in tree (**L**), smoking out opossum (**M**) which jumps into basket (**N**), pulling rope (**O**) and lifting cage (**P**), allowing woodpecker (**Q**) to chew wood from pencil (**R**), exposing lead. Emergency knife (**S**) is always handy in case opossum or the woodpecker gets sick and can't work.

Strange Inventions

by Patricia Grossman

A strange idea might be just what you need to make your life more fun. Find out how some people used their ideas to make new inventions.

Have you ever wanted to invent a machine that would make your life easier and more fun? How about a robot that would clean up your room and make your bed? It could even feed and walk your dog while you're out playing ball.

Such an invention may sound a little wacky, or "far-out," but who knows? It might just work. An invention may start off with an idea that just pops into someone's head. Most of the time, however, the inventor has to do a lot of thinking to come up with an idea that really works.

Some inventions are made just for having fun. A man from Japan thought of a special fan to help his bike move more quickly. To make it go faster, all he had to do was tie the fan to his back. This would also work for skaters and skiers.

Rube Goldberg was someone who had fun with inventions. He didn't really build the inventions. Instead, he drew pictures to show how they would work. He took an ordinary way to do something and figured out a wacky way to do it. It wasn't the best way to do something, but it was fun to read about. One of his inventions is a pencil sharpener. To use it, you need more than just a pencil and a knife. Look under the picture on page 117 for Rube Goldberg's instructions for using his invention.

Some inventions make you laugh just thinking about them. Have you seen a coat built for two? The coat looks like any coat you might wear. But if you snap here and unsnap there, you have a coat that two people can wear. Think how cozy it would feel to share a coat with your best friend. Think about the looks you would get as you walk to school!

You've heard of windshield wipers, but have you ever seen "glasses-shield" wipers? When rain gets on their glasses, people have trouble seeing. Why couldn't they wear glasses with wipers on them? The wipers could clear away the rain when a small motor is started.

Sometimes people think up strange ways to help them sell something. Robert Martino had an idea for using fish to sell things. He made shirts for fish to wear. These shirts had holes through which fish could put their fins. Messages were printed on the shirts that read "Joe's Fish Tanks," or "Samantha's Pet Store." Anyone who read the message would know where to buy pets or fish.

Sometimes an invention can make work easier. Before Hans Birch-Iensen invented the automatic egg counter, he had to count the number of eggs his hens were laying each day. The hens wore his egg counters around their necks. All he had to do was check the egg counters to see how many eggs to gather.

There are some unusual inventions that really help people. Suppose you are a person with impaired vision. You can hardly recognize your friends until they are right in front of you. A pair of TV glasses would really help. These glasses look just like sunglasses. The lenses look like TV screens. To use your TV glasses, you'd wear a cable joined to your belt. The cable works like a TV camera. It puts clear pictures of what's in front of you onto the lenses. Then you'd be able to see clearly.

People probably have been thinking up inventions since the beginning of time. Some of the inventions get built. Others never do. Maybe you could think up an amazing invention of your own!

Comprehension

1. Which invention in the article is your favorite and why?

2. Which invention do you think is most strange and why?

3. What would you like to invent to help people or for fun?

Dictation

1

2

3   4

5   6

7   8

9   10

11

12

13

Vowel-Consonant Unit är as in car *(Armadillo)*

The letters *ar* can rhyme with *car*, but not if there is a signal as in *care*, or a double *r* as in *carry*.

_____   as in *armadillo*

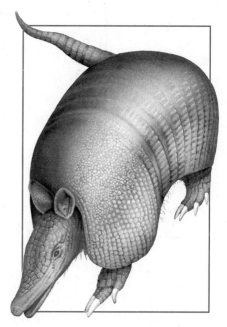

Review of Sounds

Say these sounds:

1. igh   a_   ch   i_   sh

2. u_   ė   o_   ur   e_

Give two sounds for each of these spellings:

1. s   ow   th   ew   x

2. u_e   g   ea   c

Give three sounds for the letter *y*.

är   är

är   är

When you have finished tracing and writing the new spellings, cover what you have done. Then try to write them on the extra lines without looking at the Sound Spelling Cards or the sounds page.

Reading Words

1. star   start   cart   harm

2. stark   tarnish (<u>tar</u>′ nish)   varnish (<u>var</u>′ nish)   shark

3. ditch   pitch   rich

4. far   farm   farmer (<u>farm</u>′ er)   alarm (ȧ·<u>larm</u>′)

5. harder (<u>hard</u>′ er)   hardest (<u>hard</u>′ ėst)

6. bitten (<u>bit</u>′ tėn)   biting (<u>bit</u>′ ing)

7. ever (ĕv′ er)   seven (<u>sĕv</u>′ ėn)

8. guar<u>ds</u>   **12.** carry (<u>car</u>′ ry)

9. harass (hȧr′ ass)   **13.** polar (<u>po</u>′ lar)

10. cardinal (<u>car</u>′ dĭ·nal)   **14.** margin (<u>mar</u>′ gin)

11. Arctic (<u>Arc</u>′ tic)   **15.** experience (ex·<u>pe</u>′ rï·ėnce)

Can you find three words with **arr** in them?
Do you hear the sound **ar** as in **car** in all of these words?

16. momentum (mo•<u>men</u>′ tum)

17. nutrient (<u>nu</u>′ tri•ent)

18. flexible (<u>flex</u>′ i•ble)

19. illuminate (il•<u>lum</u>′ in•ate)

20. benefactor (<u>bĕn</u>′ ė•fac•tȯr)

21. Native Americans (<u>Na</u>′ tĭve Ȧ•<u>mer</u>′ ĭ•can<u>s</u>)

22. antibiotic (an•ti•bi•<u>ot</u>′ ic)

23. Antarctic (Ant•<u>arc</u>′ tic)

24. transparent (trans•<u>par</u>′ ent)

25. remarkable (rė•<u>mark</u>′ a•ble)

Proverbs

1. Every day gives you another chance.

2. Let sleeping dogs lie.

Shark!

Sharks are fish that swim mostly in warm seas. There are about 350 kinds of sharks. All sharks are not the same size. The whale shark is the biggest. It is about 49 feet long. The smallest shark is only about 6 inches long.

Sharks have extra sets of teeth. If they bite something and a tooth falls out, a new tooth takes its place.

Many people are afraid of sharks. They know that sharks will bite people. But most people are safe. Every year sharks bite only about 100 people. Most of those people live.

It's best to stay safe. When you are at the beach, don't wade too far out in the waves. If you go sailing, stay in the sailboat. Stay away from sharks and they will stay away from you.

Words to Watch

know

whale

shark

1. Which shark is the biggest of all?

2. Find out what *redundant* or *redundancy* means. How does it apply to sharks?

3. Highlight the two ways the story gives to avoid sharks.

4. Are sharks bad animals?

Lending a Paw

by Sue Boulais

Did you know dogs have been helping people for a long, long time? Take a look at some of the ways people and dogs make great teams.

Do you have a pet dog? If you do, you know that dogs are great playmates to have around. You can teach them to do tricks and play games with you. But you have to take care of them. Not only do you have to play with them, but you also have to feed, bathe, and take them for walks.

There are millions of pet dogs in the world. Many of them are far more than friends and playmates. Some dogs work with people as well. These special dogs are called working dogs and have been partners with people for a long time. They are called upon to do all kinds of work for their owners. They can be trained to do just about any hard job, sometimes doing it even better than people can.

One kind of working dog is the search-and-rescue dog. These dogs hunt wherever people might be lost or hurt. Aja is a German shepherd who gets excited about her job. With her handler, she spends many hours a week learning how to rescue people. Together, they trudge through bad snowstorms, mud slides, and deep woods. Aja uses her keen sense of smell to help find a person who is in trouble. She works more quickly and covers more area than people would if they were working by themselves. As her reward, she has fun playing with her owner after their work is done.

Some working dogs do a lot of sniffing around! Sniffers, like Larry, are smaller dogs that can fit into places where people can't fit. Larry is a beagle. He spends his days around or under people's houses and buildings looking for termites or ants. His job is to find the insects' nests before they eat holes in wooden walls of buildings.

Many working dogs use their eyes and ears, paws and teeth to help their partners in very special ways. They spend four to six months being specially trained to make their owners' lives safer. After they are trained, they go to live with a person who needs their special skills. Because their jobs are so important, they stay very close to their owners at all times. They can go some places where dogs are not usually allowed.

Imagine a hearing aid that runs on four legs instead of batteries! That's how important hearing ear dogs, like Oscar, can be. Before he was trained to be a hearing ear, he was just a regular dog. Now, he knows sign language! He was picked for the job because he was friendly, young, and alert. When the smoke alarm sounds, or the phone rings, he alerts his owner. He is trained to hear sounds his owner can't hear.

Just as hearing ear dogs are specially trained to hear for their owners, guide dogs also have important jobs to do for their owners who are vision impaired. Sometimes Cindy, a golden retriever, may not move when her owner gives a command. That's because Cindy sees something her owner cannot see. It's Cindy's job to guide her owner around trouble. She can also pick up something her owner has dropped or even open doors.

Another kind of working dog is a service dog. Ivy is a special friend to her owner who can't use her arms and legs. Before Ivy came to help, her owner couldn't do things like turn on lights or open and close doors. But all that has changed. Ivy lends her paws to help out. She even goes to school with her owner so she can carry books and supplies.

But whether dogs are friends or playmates, hearing ears or seeing eyes, sniffers or service dogs, they are always ready to "lend a paw." It's good to know we can depend on dogs to help us.

Comprehension

1. In your own words, tell what you learned about how guide dogs help their owners.

2. Why do you think working dogs are so important?

3. What do you think this article is mainly about?

Dictation

1

2

3

4

5

6

7

8

9

10

11

12

13

Vowel Sound aw *(Hawk)*

This sound has two main spellings: *aw* and *au_*

_____ as in *hawk*

_____ as in *Paul*

Vowel-Consonant Unit

The letters *all* can sound two ways: *fallĕn*, *Ăllĕn*. So can the letters *al*: *always*, *Ălfrĕd*.

aw   aw

aur   aur

au_   au_

au_   au_

When you have finished tracing and writing the new spellings, cover what you have done. Then try to write them on the extra lines without looking at the Sound Spelling Cards or the sounds page.

Reading Words

1. claw	lawn	spawn	jaw<u>s</u>
2. law<u>s</u>	pau<u>s</u>e	claw<u>s</u>	dawn
3. t<u>a</u>ll	c<u>a</u>ll	squ<u>a</u>ll	sm<u>a</u>ll
4. drop	got	lock	nod
5. torn	corn	toss	cross
6. ripple (<u>rip</u>′ ple)	little (<u>lit</u>′ tle)		
7. fallen (<u>fa</u>ll′ en)	Allen (<u>Al</u>′ lėn)		

Suffixes:

-al	*-er*	*-ish*	*-ness*
-art	*-ful*	*-ly*	*-or*
-ed	*-ing*	*-ment*	*-y*

Level 2

                                       Suffixes:

8. because (be•<u>cause</u>′) _____

9. downy (<u>down</u>′ y) _____

10. automated (<u>au</u>′ to•ma•ted) _____

11. inaugurate (in•<u>aug</u>′ u•rate) _____

12. wrathful (<u>wrath</u>′ ful) _____

13. writer (<u>writ</u>′ er) _____

14. sailor (<u>sail</u>′ ȯr) _____

15. performed (per•<u>formed</u>′) _____

Suffixes:

16. prehistoric (pre·his·tor′ ic) _____

17. Spanish (Spăn′ ish) _____

18. awe-inspiring (awe-in·spīr′ ing) _____

19. awkward (awk′ ward) _____

20. ecology (e·col′ o·gy) _____

21. judgment (judg′ ment) _____

22. judicial branch (ju·dic′ ial branch) _____

23. scornfully (scorn′ ful·ly) _____

24. omnivore (om′ ni·vore) _____

25. intestines (in·tes′ tines) _____

Proverbs

1. A stitch in time saves nine.

2. A penny saved is a penny earned.

3. Experience is the best teacher.

Water, Water Everywhere?

If you think of a day without water, you'll see how it matters to have it and why we need to save it. Here are some simple things you can do to make every drop count.

When you brush your teeth, turn on the faucet just long enough to wet your brush, then turn it off. Turn it on again to rinse your brush. You'll save more than five gallons of water.

Make your toilet use less water. Fill an empty milk jug with gravel, put the lid on it, and put it in your toilet tank. You will save one to two gallons per flush. That adds up!

Take showers instead of baths. Showers use only half as much water. Using a low-flow showerhead cuts the amount of water in half again.

Don't water your lawn. Let Mother Nature take care of it.

Words to Watch

low-flow	toilet	gallons
enough	gravel	showerhead

Comprehension

1. What does "make every drop count" mean?

2. How much water does a non-conserver use to brush his/her teeth? Find the words.

3. What could you do if the milk jug won't fit in your toilet tank?

4. Find the words that tell how much water you can save per flush.

5. What does "low-flow" mean? Why would that save water?

6. What other substances should we be conserving?

Working Hard to Be a Winner

by Carol A. Josel

People who become the best at what they do usually have to work very hard. Read to find out how Debi Thomas became a winner at figure skating.

Being a champion figure skater is more than bright lights and shiny medals. Just ask Debi Thomas. She knows first-hand that becoming the best is not always fun and games. You have to be willing to work hard to be a winner.

Debi has been working hard for most of her life. One thing she's had to work on is confidence. Although she enjoys performing for her fans and competing with the best skaters, Debi hasn't always been as sure of herself as she is now.

When she was a little girl, Debi was very shy. Her mother wanted to help her get over her shyness. Together, they went to the opera, the ballet, and to ice shows. One day, Debi watched a clown skater do tricks on the ice, and Debi was amazed at what she saw. Debi decided right then she would learn to skate like that.

When she was five, Debi signed up for her first skating lesson. By the time she was nine, she had won her first prize. By the age of fourteen, she had learned the figure tests that every skater must know how to do. Her hard work was paying off.

Debi spent many hours practicing on the ice with her coach. Most kids her age probably would have been doing something else. Besides practicing six hours a day, she still had to go to school and do her homework. Sometimes Debi had to do her schoolwork in the car while her mother drove many miles each day from home to school, to the rink, and finally, back home again.

Because she wanted to be the best skater she could, Debi was willing to do what was needed. Her mom and dad worked hard to pay for skating lessons and practice time on the ice. Debi helped by sewing her own costumes and making up her own skating routines. She even used worn-out skates.

Schoolwork and skating continued to take up all Debi's time. Many skaters give up just about everything for their dreams of reaching the top of their sport. But that wasn't enough for Debi. Skating and studying helped her to find a balance in her life. After high school, she entered Stanford University and began studying to become a doctor. She knew that when her skating days were over, she would have other goals. She dreamed of opening her own sports medicine clinic and training center. There, young people could be taught and trained to be their best.

It wasn't easy to know how much time to spend studying, skating and getting ready for matches. Even her coach thought she was trying to do too much. To make more time, she decided to take fewer classes at a school closer to where she was practicing. In 1986, she won both the national and world figure skating titles. In 1988, she won a bronze medal in the Winter Olympic Games.

When the Olympics were over, Debi knew it was time to decide about her future. She could earn a living as an ice skater, or she could continue to train and try for a gold medal in the 1992 Olympics. And she still dreamed of becoming a doctor.

After thinking about her choices, Debi knew what to do. She decided to skate professionally on the weekends. During the week she would keep on going to school. The money she earned as a skater would pay her school costs.

Debi has reached some of her goals, but her sights are set on the future. There are other dreams to follow. There are new challenges to meet. The road to becoming the best is hard and full of bumps, but it's worth it. Debi knows that when you believe in yourself, you can be a winner. And Debi Thomas likes to win!

Comprehension

1. What first got Debi interested in skating?

2. What awards did Debi win?

3. After the Olympics were over, what decision did Debi have to make?

1

2

3

4

5

6

7

8

9

10

11

12

13

Vowel Sound **oi**＿ *(Coil)*

This sound has two spellings:

_____   as in *coil*

_____   as in *boy*

Review

1. What are the three different things that signals can do?

2. What are the three sounds of the letter *y*?

3. What is the spelling rule about *y*?

4. Say the sound of: aw   a̱r   e＿   a＿   ou＿

5. Say two sounds for: ow   c   ew   ea   g
                        s   th   x   u＿e

oi̇ oi̇

_oi̇ _oi̇

_oy _oy

_oy _oy

When you have finished tracing and writing the new spellings, cover what you have done. Then try to write them on the extra lines without looking at the Sound Spelling Cards or the sounds page.

Reading Words

Level 1

1. joy   join   joined   coy

2. soil   spoil   point   loyal (<u>loy</u>′ al)

3. pair   spare   stair<u>s</u>   stare

4. pay   paid   tirade (<u>ti</u>′ rade)

5. boy<u>s</u>   noi<u>s</u>e   noisy (<u>nois</u>′ y)   oil

6. peacock (<u>pea</u>′ cock)   pointer (<u>point</u>′ er)

7. nomad (<u>no</u>′ mad)   mesa (<u>me</u>′ sa)

Level 2

8. healthy (<u>hĕalth</u>′ y)

9. velocity (vel·<u>oc</u>′ ĭ·ty)

10. mineral (<u>mĭn</u>′ er·ȧl)

11. soybeans (<u>soy</u>′ bean<u>s</u>)

12. poison (<u>poi</u>′ <u>s</u>on)

13. thyroid (<u>thy</u>′ roid)

14. unemployment (un·em·<u>ploy</u>′ ment)

15. topsoil (<u>top</u>′ soil)

16. latitude (lat' i·tude)

17. impudent (im' pu·dent)

18. enemies (en' e·mies)

19. humanitarian (hu·man·i·tar' i·an)

20. microscope (mi' cro·scope)

21. policies (pol' i·cies)

22. symphonies (sym' pho·nies)

23. ebony (eb' on·y)

24. accompanied (ac·com' pa·nied)

25. autonomy (au·ton' o·my)

On this page, there are four words with a two-dot *i*. Write them and their root words on the proper blanks below.

Plurals (ending in *-es*)	**Root Word**
1. _____	_____
2. _____	_____
3. _____	_____

Past Form (ending in *-ed*)	**Root Word**
4. _____	_____

Quotations and a Proverb

1. The only way to have a friend is to be one.

—*Ralph Waldo Emerson*

2. Early to bed and early to rise, makes a man healthy, wealthy, and wise.

—*Benjamin Franklin*

3. Honesty is the best policy.

—*Proverb*

Dorothy Meets the Tin Man

excerpt from The Wonderful Wizard of Oz
by L. Frank Baum

"Did you groan?" asked Dorothy.

"Yes," answered the tin man, "I did. I've been groaning for more than a year, and no one has ever heard me before or come to help me."

"What can I do for you?" she inquired softly, for she was moved by the sad voice in which the man spoke.

"Get an oil can and oil my joints," he answered. "They are rusted so badly that I cannot move them at all; if I am well oiled I shall soon be all right again. You will find an oil can on a shelf in my cottage."

Dorothy at once ran back to the cottage and found the oil can, and then she returned and asked anxiously, "Where are your joints?"

Words to Watch

answered   heard   before

moved   anxiously   groaning

Comprehension

1. Highlight the words which will help you clarify "she was moved."

2. What was it that Dorothy didn't understand?

3. How long had the tin man been rusted?

4. What is this story about?

Time Out to Help

by Marcia K. Miller

Roberto Clemente was a great baseball player. But he knew that there was more to life than baseball. Find out what else he wanted to be during his life.

What makes baseball players really great? Some can hit the ball far with great power. Others field balls hit in their direction with little effort. A few players encourage and lead their team both on and off the field. Roberto Clemente did all these things and more. He was also a friend and helper to those who needed him.

Roberto learned early in life how to be an honest, hard worker. Whenever there was something that needed doing, he worked hard to get the job done. When his parents asked him to do something, he did what they asked and did not complain. When a neighbor needed help, Roberto would volunteer. All his friends knew they could depend on him to give his best.

After the day's work, young Roberto liked to play baseball with other kids on his block. In fact, he liked playing baseball more than anything else. He even dreamed of a chance to play for a professional team. He wanted to find a way to use playing baseball to help other people.

Finally, that chance came. He was offered a position with the Pittsburgh Pirates. He began to work hard to improve himself as a team player. It wasn't easy, but it was what Roberto felt he had to do. He also became a team leader. He showed other players how to be better. Many times he gave up his own playing time for the good of the team. It was his example for the other players that made him a useful team member. When the Pirates won the World Series, he felt proud because he had helped his team become the best.

Roberto was a special friend and helper to children. He always took time to answer questions and sign autographs after the games. He was pleased to tell them how baseball had helped him. He encouraged them to work harder to be the best they could be. Sometimes, when he got an award, he asked that the prize money be given to a hospital. That way, children who needed extra care could be helped.

After many years as a successful baseball player, Roberto also became known as a person who helped others. Some of his friends asked him to think about becoming mayor of the city where he lived. After he thought about it, he decided he would help people in other ways. He liked to work quietly to encourage friendships and good will among people. But he didn't wait to speak out when he felt he could make a difference.

One of his fondest dreams was to build a Sports City. At this sports center, the kids he cared about so much would work with good coaches and equipment. They would learn how to give their best efforts and work together as a team. They would learn values to help them in life.

But an emergency put off Roberto's dream when an earthquake shook Nicaragua in December 1972. Roberto worked to raise money for food, medicine, and clothing to help the people who needed it. He decided to go to Nicaragua to see if there was more he could do. But he never got there. The plane that carried him and the supplies crashed, and he was killed.

When news of his death became known, people were very sad. Some remembered him as a great baseball player. But many who *really* knew him remembered him as a person who was ready to help others. In his memory, Sports City was built. As he wished, it is free and open to everyone. It still reminds people to look for ways to be a friend and lend a hand.

1. In what ways did Roberto Clemente help people?

2. How did Roberto Clemente die? Where was he going?

3. What do you think made Roberto Clemente a great person to be remembered?

1

2

3

4

5

6

7

8

9

10

11

12

13

Vowel Sound ŏŏ *(Foot)*

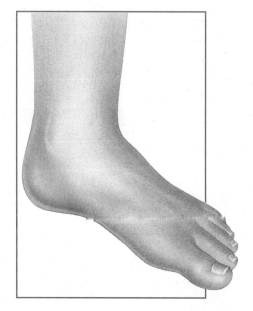

_____ as in *foot*

_____ as in *put*

ŏŏ   ŏŏ

ŏŏ   ŏŏ

ṳ   ṳ

ṳ   ṳ

When you have finished tracing and writing the new spellings, cover what you have done. Then try to write them on the extra lines without looking at the Sound Spelling Cards or the sounds page.

Reading Words

Level 1

1. good   stood   wood

   cookbook (<u>cook</u>′ book)

2. took   shook   look   nook

3. soon   zoo   room   food

4. wool   pull   full   bull

5. bush   push   put   dull

6. brook   crook   crooked (<u>crook</u>′ ėd)

7. cable (<u>ca</u>′ ble)   middle (<u>mid</u>′ dle)

8. could   should   couldn't   wouldn't

Level 2

9. mishap (<u>mis</u>′ hap)

10. output (<u>out</u>′ put)

11. merchant (<u>mer</u>′ chȧnt)

12. Kremlin (<u>Krem</u>′ lin)

13. input (<u>in</u>′ put)

14. revenge (rė·<u>venġe</u>′)

15. gravity (<u>grav</u>′ i·ty)

16. universal (u·ni·<u>ver</u>′ sal)

17. pancreas (pan' cre·as)

18. heritage (hĕr' i·tȧge)

19. hemisphere (hĕm' i·sphere)

20. sweatshops (sweat' shops)

21. puberty (pu' ber·ty)

22. ill-tempered (ill-tem' pered)

23. general (ġĕn' er·ȧl)

24. tremendous (trė·men' dȯus)

25. wavelength (wave' length)

26. sabotage (sab' o·tȧge)

Proverbs

1. Make hay while the sun shines.

2. Where there is smoke there is fire.

3. Well begun is half done.

What happens when something is badly begun? Give examples.

April Fools' Day

There's sugar in the salt shaker and salt in the sugar bowl. Someone has taken the filling out of your cream-filled cookie and put toothpaste in its place. Your friend tells you a story that is untrue. It must be April Fools' Day.

April Fools' Day, or All Fools' Day, is a day when people pull jokes on each other. People around the world play tricks. In the United States, when the joke is on you, you are called an April Fool. In France, if someone pulls a joke on you, you are called an April Fish. In Scotland, you would be called a cuckoo.

Wherever you live, April Fools' Day is a day that reminds you to make some room for fun and laughter. Now that you know that, school is over for the rest of the day.

(April Fool!)

Words to Watch

sugar   Scotland

laughter   France

156

1. Find and highlight:
   —all the contractions in the story
   —two *a_e* words
   —two *o_e* words

2. Where/how did April Fools' Day get started?

3. Highlight each pause marker in the selection.

Collecting Can Be Fun

by Debra L. Byrne

There's no better way to have fun than to enjoy a hobby. A hobby can be what you want it to be. Find out about some interesting hobbies when you read this article.

How do you like to spend your free time? Do you enjoy learning how to do something, like playing a new game or a musical instrument? Maybe you like to build things. Spending hours or even days putting together model airplanes, trains, or tiny cities may be your idea of fun.

Just about any activity that you spend your free time doing is called a hobby. Your hobby doesn't have to take up much space. You may not even need lessons or special skills. You just have to be interested enough to spend time doing it. Collecting is a favorite hobby for many people. Some have thousands of different items in their collection. They have been collecting for a long time! Others didn't start out with collecting in mind, but ended up with a hobby they really enjoy.

You might already have the start of a collection. Is there some kind of object that you really look for when you go to special places or go out to have fun? You might spend a lot of money on a collection or none at all. It depends on what you want to collect.

Some people like to collect things they find on the ground around them—like bony treasures. Danika Swanson began collecting skulls several years ago when she found her first one on her family's farm in Wisconsin. She was so interested in her bony treasure that she went to the library to learn exactly what she had found. It turned out to be a raccoon's skull. Now, her family helps her find more skulls to add to her collection. How would you like to receive a skunk's skull as a birthday surprise?

If you'd really like to begin collecting bones, there are some safety tips you need to know. Never pick up animals that have just died. Always use gloves to pick up bones that have not been cleaned. Ask an adult to help you. You also need to find out if it's OK to collect animal bones where you live.

If bone hunting isn't for you, you might want to think about collecting other objects from nature. They might be insects, feathers, or seashells. Before you know it, you'll begin to be an expert on what you collect.

Maybe you could become a rock hound. That's someone who hunts for rocks. You could look for rocks with shiny crystals, strange shapes, and different colors. Once you start looking, you'll be surprised at how many different kinds of rocks you can find just about anywhere. When you have gathered some rocks, you can arrange your collection. You might even want to start your own rock museum!

If you decide to begin rock hunting, you'll always want to keep safety in mind. Stay away from places that are too dangerous, and watch out for falling rocks. To protect your eyes, always wear safety goggles when hammering rocks.

If you don't care about rocks, what about collecting baseball cards, stuffed animals, patches, or bottle caps? You might also want to think about collecting things from different places. You could have a different kind of collection if you had a sticker, a post card, a poster, or a T-shirt from every place you've been.

These are only a few ideas to get you started. The idea is to have fun collecting. Remember, the longer you stay with your hobby, the bigger and better your collection will become.

Keep your eyes open for new things to add to it. Then look for a good way to show it off. Finally, when the word gets around that you're collecting, you'll find that your family and friends want to help.

Comprehension

1. What is your favorite hobby?

2. What are some important safety tips you learned from the article about collecting bones?

3. Make a list of the hobbies you learned about in the article.

1

2

3

4

5

6

7

8

9

10

11

12

13

Consonant Sound **n** spelled **kn_** or **gn** *(Nose)*

There is a silent letter in each of these special spellings.

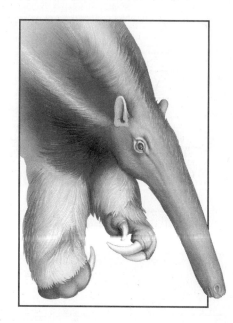

_____ = **n**   as in *know*

_____ = **n**   as in *gnaw, sign*

kn_   kn_

kn   kn

gn   gn

gn   gn

When you have finished tracing and writing the new spellings, cover what you have done. Then try to write them on the extra lines without looking at the Sound Spelling Cards or the sounds page.

Reading Words

1. no   nose   know<u>s</u>   known

2. nod   knock   not   knob

3. rap   wrap   wrapped

4. wrong   wren   wrench   wreath

5. Nat   gnat   gnaw   gnome

6. lĭmb   clīmb   cōmb   bŏmb

7. crumb   dumb   thumb   benign (be·<u>nign</u>′)

Now circle each silent letter.

Level 2

8. wri<u>the</u>

9. wriggle (<u>wrig</u>′ gle)

10. gnarled

11. wreckage (<u>wreck</u>′ àge)

12. vertical (<u>ver</u>′ ti·cal)

13. knotty (<u>knot</u>′ ty)

14. kneecap (<u>knee</u>′ cap)

15. knuckle (<u>knuck</u>′ le)

Now circle each silent letter.

16. precipitate (pre·cip′ i·tate)

17. universe (ū′ ni·verse)

18. astronauts (as′ trȯ·nauts)

19. Austria (Aus′ trï·à)

20. Australia (Aus·tral′ ïà)

21. hydrocarbon (hy′ dro·car·bon)

22. familiar (fà·mĭl′ ïar)

23. semicircle (sem′ ï·cir·cle)

24. parallelogram (par·a·lel′ o·gram)

25. industrial (in·dus′ trï·àl)

Two-dot *i* says *y_* in **Australïa**. Circle four other words in which it says *y_*.

Quotation

Failure is the opportunity to begin again, more intelligently.
—*Henry Ford*

A Helping Hand

They help us when we are sick and teach us how to stay well. They know a lot and are much needed. Who are they? Nurses.

Nurses work day and night to make sure those in need have help. One way they help is to give patients medicine when it is needed. The medicine is used to help heal an infection or take away pain.

Nurses also help doctors who operate on people. To do this, nurses need to know a lot about the human body.

They have many skills. Nurses have a kind manner and they take the time to listen to people with problems. This makes nurses very important to all of us.

Words to Watch

patients

medicine

infection

1. Find and write all the words in the story that tell what nurses do.

2. Now find and write the words that describe the qualities nurses have.

3. Can you find out what the study of the human body is called?

4. Can nurses teach?

The Milk Carton Derby

by Sue Boulais

Would you try to build a boat from old milk cartons? People in Seattle, Washington, do. Every year they have a special boat race called the Milk Carton Derby.

How much milk does it take to float a boat? No, this question isn't a joke. Some people ask this question every year.

Every year, Seattle, Washington, has a festival called Seafair. People come from many places to have fun and good times. The favorite part of the fair is the Milk Carton Derby. In the Derby, people race boats that are made from milk cartons!

You may be asking a question now. What kind of boat can you make from milk cartons? The answer is *any kind*. Some people have made long, wide milk-carton boats. Others have made boats shaped like an elephant or a big wheel or an airplane. But many of the boats are small, just right for one or two grown-ups or children. That's right. Many of the racers are children.

That sounds like a lot of fun, doesn't it? Any milk-carton boat racer can tell you that it is. And some of the fun comes before the racers even float their boats.

That's because the racers have to plan and build their milk-carton boats! The fun starts when the racers ask *themselves* some questions. What kind of boat will I build? How long will it be? How wide will it be? How many people will be on it? Answering these questions helps racers plan their boats.

Once racers have planned their milk-carton boats, they ask themselves more questions. What size milk cartons am I going to use to build my boat? Which size would be best? Will I buy my milk in big cartons or small ones? Should I maybe buy the size in between?

When the racers answer these questions, they start to collect empty milk cartons. THAT's when the racers find out how much milk it's going to take to float their boats!

The fun goes on. As the racers finish the milk, they wash the carton out. Then they begin to pile up their cartons.

At last, the racers have all the empty milk cartons they need. Then there is another question. How can they put the cartons together? Empty cartons can be tied or stuck together many different ways.

Of course, putting the cartons together makes more fun. Racers and their friends start to work on the cartons. They work together building the boats. They work together right down to the last step—waterproofing the milk cartons.

At last it's the opening day of Seafair. Everyone is ready for the Milk Carton Derby. Racers pull or carry their boats out to Green Lake. Today they have only two questions. Will my boat float? Who will win the Milk Carton Derby this year?

The racers aren't the only ones asking those questions. Everyone at Seafair wants to know whose boat will float and who will win the races. People line up all around the lake.

As each race begins, everyone finds out right away whose boat floats. Some boats sink right away. Some racers didn't make their boats waterproof. Other racers didn't put enough milk cartons together to hold themselves up.

But many boats are floating and racing! Some racers paddle. Some kick with their feet. Some row. But everyone, racers and watchers, has a good time. Who will win? By now, everyone is having such fun that no one really cares anymore.

Besides, there's always next year.

Just look at all those floating milk cartons. There must be hundreds. Don't you wonder just how much milk those racers *did* drink to float their boats?

Comprehension

1. What steps do the boat-makers go through to make their milk-carton boats?

2. Where is the Milk Carton Derby held?

3. Do all the boats float? If not, why?

Dictation

1

2

3   **4**

5   **6**

7   **8**

9   **10**

11

12

13

Special Pattern wȯr_ as in work

(Note: *or* after *w* usually says *er*.)
In words like **worthy**, the letters **wor** sound like the word **were**.

_____   as in **worthy**

wȯr   wȯr

wȯr   wȯr

When you have finished tracing and writing the new spelling, cover what you have done. Then try to write it on the extra lines without looking at the Sound Spelling Cards or the sounds page.

Reading Words

1. word   cord   worm

   earthworm (<u>earth</u>′ worm)

2. worth   forth

3. worse   horse   hoarse

4. world   worst   worship (<u>wor</u>′ ship)

5. worry (<u>wor</u>′ ry)   sorry (<u>sor</u>′ ry)

6. worthless (<u>worth</u>′ less)   worthwhile (<u>worth</u> while)

7. evaporate (e·<u>vap</u>′ o·rate)   silkworm (<u>silk</u>′ worm)

8. knelt

9. kneeling (<u>kneel</u>′ ing)

10. knighthood (<u>knight</u>′ hood)

11. comparison (com·<u>par</u>′ i·son)

12. shelter (<u>shel</u>′ ter)

13. predator (<u>pred</u>′ at·or)

14. cardiac muscle (<u>car</u>′ di·ac <u>mus</u>′ cle)

15. Aztecs (<u>Az</u>′ tecs)

16. receptor (re·<u>cep</u>′ tor)

17. dialect (<u>dī</u>′ à·lect)

18. decompose (de·com·<u>pose</u>′)

19. orient (<u>or</u>′ i·ent)

20. corporal (<u>cor</u>′ pò·ràl)

21. porcelain (<u>por</u>′ cè·làin)

22. formula (<u>for</u>′ mū·là)

23. carbon dioxide (<u>car</u>′ bon di·<u>ox</u>′ ide)

24. intersecting (<u>in</u>′ ter·sec·ting)

25. congruent (con·<u>gru</u>′ ent)

Proverbs

1. Every cloud has a silver lining.

2. April showers bring May flowers.

3. A trip of a thousand miles begins with a single step.

War of the Worlds

No one had TVs in 1938. People listened to the radio. Every night, families and friends gathered around to listen to their favorite programs. On one of those nights, they got one of the worst scares of their lives.

A radio announcer named Orson Welles told America that Martians had landed on Earth. To make things worse, he said that the Martians were blowing up towns and cities.

People who heard the report thought that it was true. They thought they were in great danger, and they panicked. Finally, the police went to the radio station and made Mr. Welles tell the people that the story was not true. He said he was sorry for scaring people so badly.

Today, Orson Welles' story is known as one of the best tricks ever played. But many people listening that night in 1938 thought it was the worst trick.

Words to Watch

friends	Martians
great	panicked

1. Highlight the word that tells what people did when they heard the story. Write three words that would describe their behavior.

2. What became of Orson Welles' story?

3. What else is Orson Welles famous for?

4. How was it possible for one person to convince so many people that something terrible was happening when it really wasn't?

Wheels, Wheels, Wheels

by Patricia Grossman

What kinds of wheels do you know about? What are some wheels that you use every day? Read to find out about new ways to use wheels.

How many ways can a wheel turn? The real answer to that is *four*. It can turn left, or it can turn right. It can roll to the front, or it can roll to the back.

But when it comes to having fun, a wheel can turn you into someone you dream about. It can make you a roller skater, a skateboard or bicycle rider, a race car driver, or even a skate sailor!

Every day after school many children all over the world move over sidewalks on roller skates. Did you ever wonder who first had the idea of roller skates? Just think about it. Once, a long time ago, someone thought it would be fun to use feet to *ride*, not just walk.

The first skate wheels were made of wood. Metal wheels came later. Today, many children use skates with plastic wheels. The best part about today's wheels is that they can turn you into a person with all kinds of new things to do.

Walking on a sandy beach is fun. But if you've ever done it, you know it's also hard work. Well, "monster skates" can fix that. Like the wheels on cars and trucks, monster skates have wheels filled with air. They let monster skates carry you easily over the sand.

Do you think you would like to ski? You can do it even if you live in a place with little snow. Skates called Rollerblades can turn you into a skier! They come with poles just like the ones skiers use. These skates can make you feel as if you are crossing a big snowy field.

Now, think about sailing. Think about bright sails in the wind. Think about warm sun and wind in your face.

Did you know you can feel all this without ever stepping into a boat? You don't even need water! All you need are a sail and a pair of roller skates. The sail is taller and wider than you are, but you can hold it in your hand. Just turn the sail to make your skates go wherever you want. And you'll go *fast!*

Wheels can also turn under water. Did you have a bicycle when you were three or four years old? Now you might think that kind of bicycle is for a baby. But children older than you ride bicycles that size.

They race them along the bottom of swimming pools. Yes, they race under water. But they must carry air in a bottle on their backs. That air lets them breathe under the water.

As you might guess, people need to be very careful with some of these new wheels. They must learn to use the wheels in a safe way and should have help when using them.

Wheels have been with us for a long, long time. And in all those years, the wheel has turned for us in many new ways. Wheels have even turned for us on the moon!

1. What ways have you used wheels?

2. What are three things you remember from the story?

3. Which new kind of wheels do you like best and why?

Dictation

1

2

3

4

5

6

7

8

9

10

11

12

13

Consonant Sound **sh** spelled _ti_ or _ci_ *(Shell)*

The mark shows two letters working together to say **sh** in the middle of a word.

sh

_____ as in ***nation***

_____ as in ***facial***

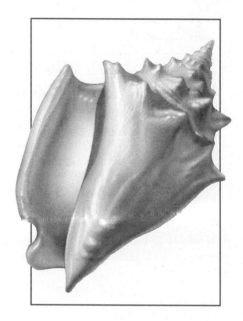

Consonant Sound _s_ *(Sander)*

The mark shows that this is not a regular sound of **s**. In some dictionaries, this sound is respelled **zh**.

_____ as in ***pleasure***

sh   sh   _ci_   _ci_

sh   sh   _ci   _ci_

_ti_   _ti_   _s_   _s_

_ti   _ti_   _s   _s_

When you have finished tracing and writing the new spellings, cover what you have done. Then try to write them on the extra lines without looking at the Sound Spelling Cards or the sounds page.

Reading Words

1. nation (na′ tion)   suction (suc′ tion)

2. fraction (frac′ tion)   addition (ad·di′ tion)

3. subtract (sub·tract′)   subtraction (sub·trac′ tion)

4. multiplication (mul·ti·pli·ca′ tion)

5. divisor (di·vi′ sor)   division (di·vi′ sion)

6. operation (op·er·a′ tion)   evidence (ev′ i·dence)

7. quotient (quo′ tient)   patient (pa′ tient)

8. solution (so·lu′ tion)   12. stations (sta′ tions)

9. Asia (A′ sia)   13. ancient (an′ cient)

10. numeration (nu·mer·a′ tion)   14. visions (vi′ sions)

11. evaporation (e·vap·or·a′ tion) 15. contraption (con·trap′ tion)

Suffixes: *-ȧl*   *-iȧl*   *-iȧn*   *-iȯn*

Level 3

	Related Words	Suffixes
16. creation (crē·ā′ ṭi̇on)	_____	_____
17. inflation (in·flā′ ṭi̇on)	_____	_____
18. musician (mu·sĭ′ ci̇an)	_____	_____
19. pollination (pol·lin·a′ ṭi̇on)	_____	_____
20. spatial (spā′ ṭi̇al)	_____	_____
21. Emancipation Proclamation (E·man·ci·pa′ ṭi̇on Proc·la·ma′ ṭi̇on)	_____	_____
22. mathematician (math·e·mȧ·ti′ ci̇an)	_____	_____
23. demonstration (dem·ȯn·stra′ ṭi̇on)	_____	_____
24. confusion (cȯn·fu′ si̇on)	_____	_____
25. occasional (ȯc·ca′ si̇on·ȧl)	_____	_____

Proverbs

1. Great oaks from little acorns grow.

2. Don't count your chickens before they're hatched.

3. The grass is always greener on the other side of the fence.

Television

Here are some little-known facts about something that most of us see every day.

The first TV show was really just a drawing of Felix the Cat standing on a box. The picture had no color. It was a black and white drawing.

Cartoons have always been popular, and not just with kids. In 1960, most of the people who watched "The Flintstones" were grown-ups. Today, grown-ups still watch certain cartoons.

The world's biggest TV is 131 feet by 82 feet. It's so big you can watch a program on it from half a mile away!

Kids watch more than six and one-half hours of TV every day. That comes to 98 days each year.

The average kid in the U.S. watches about 50 TV commercials each day.

Words to Watch

hours   commercials   popular

1. How big is the world's biggest television? Find the words. Can you find out where it is?

2. How much time does the average kid spend watching TV? Find all the answers. If a commercial lasts one minute, how much time is that out of each day of watching TV? How many days out of one year?

3. Who watches cartoons? Find all the answers.

4. Keep track of how much TV you watch for the next 7 days. See if you fit the pattern.

A Design for "The Wall"

by Carol A. Josel

What if one of your ideas became famous? How would you feel if everyone in the whole country had an opinion about your idea? Read to see how one young woman handled all those opinions.

Two black stone walls rise out of the ground. Each wall is two hundred feet long. They meet to form a "V." "That won't be much of a memorial," many people thought. "There's not much to see."

That was back in 1982. Today we know they were wrong. More than 10,000 people visit the Vietnam Veterans Memorial each day. That's more visitors than almost any other place in Washington, D.C.

Many people were against the war in Vietnam while it was going on. Even friends did not agree about it. When the war ended, there were no happy parades. Instead, people tried to forget. Years later, though, many needed to remember those who had given their lives in Vietnam.

A memorial was to be built in Washington. A contest was held to choose its design. Anyone could enter. Maya Ying Lin was one of them. Many of the designs were made by architects. But Maya Lin wasn't an architect yet. She was only a student. She had one year to go in college before she could even begin taking classes to become an architect. But her design won the $20,000 prize.

Maya had not always planned to be an architect. When she left her home in Ohio to enter college, she was not sure what she wanted to be. She took some photography classes and loved them. She was good at designing and making clothes. She liked to cook. But in the end she decided to become an architect. She says, "One day, I was just staring up at the ceiling, at all the lines and painting on it. Suddenly, I decided I was going to be an architect. Just like that."

When it came time to design the memorial, she knew just what she wanted. She chose black stone because to her it is gentler than white. It is soft on the eyes. When polished, it turns into a mirror. The memorial would be a stone mirror with names cut into it. "The point," she said, "is to see yourself reflected in the names." Those names belong to the men and women who died, or are still missing, in Vietnam. Most people wanted them listed alphabetically, but not Maya. She chose to list them in the order in which they were killed or lost. She had a good reason. "If you were in the war," she explained, "you could find your time and a few people you knew. You're remembering a moment in history."

Many people thought she was wrong. They hated her wall. That hurt Maya very much. She never stopped studying, though.

At that time, she was going to school in Connecticut and going to Washington every weekend to work on the memorial. After a while, it got to be too much for her. She decided to finish school later. While the memorial was being built, she took a job with a Boston architect. When the memorial was finished, she returned to school. She is now an architect in New York City.

The memorial that she designed is now known as "The Wall." There are always visitors there, even at night. They go to find the name of a loved one. They touch the name cut into the black stone. Some make a rubbing of the name using paper and crayons or chalk. Some light candles and leave them there. Some leave a note or flowers. Maya Ying Lin's memorial has done what she meant it to do. It has helped us accept.

1. Would you like to visit the Vietnam Veterans Memorial? Why?

2. List five things you can remember about "The Wall."

3. Decide on something for which you'd like to make a memorial. Write about what it will look like.

Dictation

1

2

3

4

5

6

7

8

9

10

11

12

13

Consonant Sound **m** spelled **_mb** *(Monkey)*

_____ = **m**   as in ***comb***

Consonant Sound **f** spelled **ph** *(Fan)*

In words from the Greek, ***ph*** has the sound of ***f***. There is no sound of ***p*** or of ***h*** in ***ph***.

_____ = **f**   as in ***phone***

Consonant Sound **k** spelled **c̄h**   *(Camera)*

In words from the Greek, ***ch*** has the sound of ***k***. In the word list, these words have a bar above the **c** to show that this is not a regular sound of ***ch***.

_____ = k   as in ***chorus***

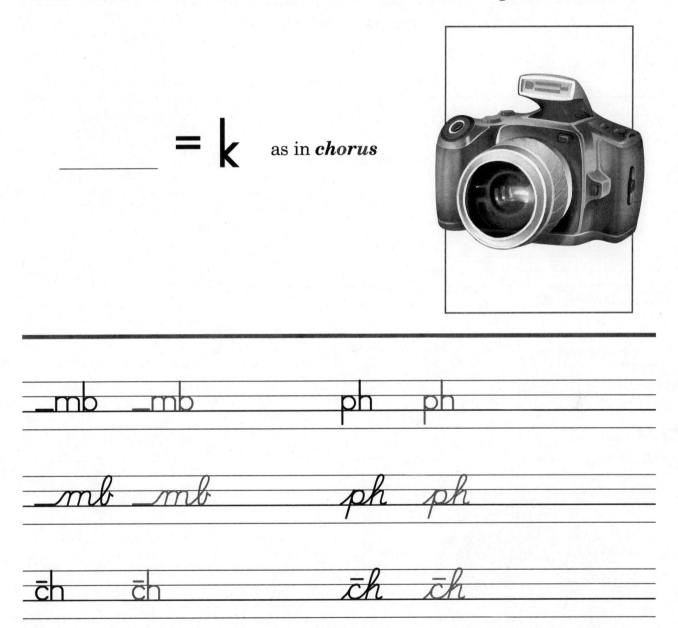

_mb   _mb   ph   ph

_mb   _mb   ph   ph

c̄h   c̄h   c̄h   c̄h

When you have finished tracing and writing the new spellings, turn the page. Then try to write them on the extra lines without looking at the Sound Spelling Cards or the sounds pages.

193

Reading Words

Watch for Greek *ph* or *ch*.

1. chorus (c̄hor′ us)   c̄hrome   monarch (mon′ arc̄h)

2. c̄hord   cord

3. photograph (phō′ tȯ·graph)

4. autograph (au′ tȯ·graph)

5. paraphrase (par′ ȧ·phrase)

6. usually (ū′ s̠ū·ȧl·ly)

7. line graph

Level 2

8. sediment (sed′ i·ment)

9. amphibian (am·phi′ bi·an)

10. Declaration of Independence (Dec·lȧ·ra′ tiȯn of In·de·pen′ dence)

11. constitution (con·sti·tu′ tiȯn)

12. scientist (scī′ ėn·tist)

13. diaphragm (di′ ȧ·phragm)

14. equation (e·qua′ tiȯn)

15. cholera (chŏl′ er·a)

16. character (chăr′ ac·ter)

17. physician (phy̆·sĭ′ cian)

18. circumscribe (cir′ cum·scribe)

19. oxygen (ŏx′ y̆·gen)

20. chlorophyll (chlor′ o·phyll)

21. holograph (hol′ o·graph)

22. esophagus (e·soph′ a·gus)

23. photosynthesis (pho·to·syn′ the·sis)

24. chromosome (chro′ mo·some)

In words from the Greek, the sound *ĭ* is often spelled with a *y*. Circle three such words above.

Proverbs

1. Look before you leap.

2. Never put off till tomorrow what you can do today.

3. One good turn deserves another.

Thumbs Up!

Look at your hand. Look at your fingers. Now look at that short, thick thing we call a thumb. You are looking at one amazing and very useful body part.

Think about the many ways you use your thumbs every day. Your thumb helps you to hold a pen or pencil, or a comb. If you dropped a crumb of chocolate cake on your plate, it would be hard to pick up without your thumb. How could you climb a tree without thumbs? How could you grab the limbs? Try to do any of these things without your thumbs. It's a little awkward.

We also use our thumbs to communicate. Did you ever hear the saying "thumb your nose"? How about "thumb a ride," "all thumbs," or "twiddle your thumbs"? Without thumbs, how would movie critics tell us which movies they like and don't like?

So here's thumbs up to thumbs!

Words to Watch

twiddle   awkward

movie   movies

197

1. Find and write all the different ways the thumb is used.

2. What does "twiddle your thumbs" mean?

3. Do humans have an "opposable thumb"? What does that mean? Do any animals have it?

Try It! You Might Like It!

by Sue Boulais

Do you always have the same thing for breakfast? What about your lunch? Is it always the same, too? To relax and stretch your mind, here are some ideas that may be new to you.

Do you have a favorite sandwich—peanut butter and banana, say? Every time you eat one, your friend asks, "How can you eat *that*?" And you answer, "Why don't you try one? You might like it!"

The world is full of wonderful foods. Yet most people eat only a few. They don't want to try the rest. The rest seem too strange.

But food that seems strange to one person is someone else's favorite. What many people forget is that their favorite food might be odd if they hadn't decided to try it!

Every day, you and your friends eat a favorite sandwich for lunch. You may have a favorite fruit, too, an apple or an orange. And you probably drink fresh, cold milk.

But in many other countries, no one except babies ever drinks milk, and sandwiches aren't a favorite food for lunch. In Japan, many children's lunch is cooked fish, hot rice, fried vegetables, and tea. Boys and girls in Thailand like fish and rice, too. Children on the island of Samoa also like fish, but a real favorite is turtle meat.

Many children who don't live near the ocean eat their favorite vegetables for lunch. Some Africans eat corn soup with vegetables leaves. Others choose from beans, peas, sweet potatoes, and tomatoes. Some Saudi Arabians stuff their vegetable with rice and other vegetables. Iranian girls and boys cook their vegetables with fruit, nuts, a little meat, and plenty of rice.

Do these lunches sound unusual to you? Try one! You might like it!

What do you like for breakfast? Toast and eggs are favorites of many people in the United States, Canada, and Great Britain. Children in Holland and Norway might also have eggs. But in Holland, cold meat and cheese are breakfast favorites, too. In Norway, add fish and reindeer meat. Our young Japanese friends would eat their eggs with rice or seaweed. But even better, Japanese boys and girls like a breakfast of soup, baked fish, and pickles.

In Nigeria, girls and boys start the day with a hot soup made from red and green peppers and other vegetables. Cheese, olives, bread, and honey are on some breakfast tables in Turkey and Greece. Children in Indonesia wake up to the smell of fried rice and chilies.

Strange breakfasts, you say? Try one! You might like it!

What's your favorite dinner? Soup of one kind or another is a great favorite with many children. German boys and girls have their soup with buttered vegetables. Hungarians put hot spices in their soups, and Spanish children often use sausage. Some African children eat a soup of dried meat, beans, and other vegetables. Others make soup of peanuts and onions with meat or fish.

So the next time someone offers you a strange or unusual food, remember that it could become your new favorite. It may be strange or unusual only because you haven't tried it yet. Try it! You might like it!

1. What is your favorite food?

2. Name some foods that your family often serves, and tell if you like or dislike them.

3. Have you ever tried a food from another country? Describe it.

4. Why would foods differ from country to country?

1 _____

2 _____

3 _____

4 _____

5 _____

6 _____

7 _____

8 _____

9 _____

10 _____

11 _____

12 _____

13 _____

Card	Spellings	Terms	Sample Words
Long a	ā a_e ai_ _ay	a mark a blank e ai blank blank ay	table make, bake train, claim play, say
Basketball	b	b	balloon
Camera	c k _ck	c k blank ck, green box	cake kitchen check
Dinosaur	d	d	danger
Long e	ē ee ea _y _ï_	e mark double e ea blank y blank two dot i blank	me feet, sleet leap, feat happy, baby babies, machine
Fan	f ph	f ph	feather elephant
Gopher	g	g	gas, get
Hound	h_	h blank	hot, heavy
Long i	ī i_e _igh _ȳ	i mark i blank e blank igh blank y mark	pilot, I bite, pile light, high cry, sky
Jump	j_ _dge ġe ġi ġy	j blank blank dge, green box one dot ge one dot gi one dot gy	jam, jet fudge gem giant gym
Camera	k c _ck	k c blank ck, green box	kitten cat sick, tack

Card	Spellings	Terms	Sample Words
Lion	l	l	lamp
Monkey	m	m	match, my
Nose	n kn_ gn	n kn blank gn	never know, knife gnat, sign
Long o	ō o_e oa_ _ōw	o mark o blank e oa blank blank ow mark	Oklahoma bone soap, float throw, low
Popcorn	p	p	paper, pillow
Quacking	qu_	qu blank	quick, quill
Robot	r wr_ er ir ur	r wr blank er ir ur	road, ram wrong river bird turn
Sausages	s ce ci cy	s ce ci cy	sister, same cent cinder bicycle
Timer	t	t	tempest, time
Long u	ū u_e _ew	u mark u blank e blank ew	future, using use, cute few, mew
Vacuum Cleaner	v	v	voice, save
Washer	w_	w blank	wash, will
Exit Sign	_x _x̲	blank x, green box blank x voice bar, green box	extra, box exist, exam
Yak	y_	y blank	yellow, yes

Card	Spellings	Terms	Sample Words
Zipper	z _s	z blank s voice bar	zoo, zebra hose
Lamb	a_	a blank	flat, tap
Hen	e_ _ĕa_	e blank blank ea blank mark	pet, ten bread, head
Pig	i_	i blank	sit, pill
Fox	o_	o blank	hot, pot
Tugboat	u_ ȧ ė ȯ	u blank one dot a one dot e one dot o	thumb, bus around loaded wagon, come
Goo	o͞o ṳ̄ u_e _ew	double o long mark two dot u mark u blank e blank ew	boot, goose truth rude blew, chew
Foot	o͝o _ṳ_	double o long curved mark blank two dot u blank	foot, book put, pudding
Coil	oi_ _oy	oi blank blank oy	soil, boil toy, boy
Cow	ow ou_	ow ou blank	cowl, owl ouch, out
Hawk	aw au_ ạll	aw au blank a two dot	saw, raw Paul, caught tall, fall
Armadillo	är	two dot ar	park, car
Shell	sh _ṭi_ _çi_	sh blank ti blank mark blank ci blank mark	ship, show nation special
Whale	wh_	wh blank	white

Card	Spellings	Terms	Sample Words
Chipmunk	**ch** **_tch**	ch blank tch, green box	chest, church catch
Thing	**th** **th**	th th voice bar	thick, tooth this, them
Gong	**_ng**	blank ng	sing, ring
Sander	**_s_**	blank s blank mark	vision, treasure

The last card (No. 44) is the Signal Card. The signals are **e**, **i**, **y**. They serve two purposes:

1. They can signal through one consonant to tell the preceding vowel to say its name.

              shade   shiny   babies

2. The signals following g or c soften those letters.

        ge — gem   gi — giant   gy — gym
        ce — cent   ci — cinder   cy — bicycle

Notes